CAT SENSE
INSIDE THE FELINE MIND

CAT SENSE
INSIDE THE FELINE MIND

Akif Pirinçci
and
Rolf Degen

Translated from the German by Anthea Bell

FOURTH ESTATE · *London*

'We can never understand the soul of the cat fully without becoming cats ourselves.'

(St George Mivart, leading nineteenth-century expert on cats)

First published in Great Britain in 1994 by
Fourth Estate Limited
289 Westbourne Grove
London W11 2QA

Copyright 1994 by Goldmann Verlag
This translation copyright 1994 by Anthea Bell

The right of Anthea Bell to be identified as the translator of this work has been asserted by her in accordance with the Copyright, Designs and Patents Act 1988.

A catalogue record for this book is available from the British Library.

ISBN 1–85702–255–6

Typeset by York House Typographic Ltd
Printed and bound in Great Britain by
Biddles Ltd, Guildford and King's Lynn

Contents

Foreword
by Francis
(Who will be known to readers of Akif Pirinçci's crime novels
as the feline hero of *Felidae* and *Felidae on the Road*, and a stern
critic of human nature)

*What a nerve! I mean, talk about an enterprise doomed to failure from
the outset. Here we have a couple of those hairless humans who think
they know it all, although from our feline point of view their sensory
organs suggest curiosities from the pre-industrial era of prosthesis
construction – and they claim to have discovered our secrets. As if
that wasn't enough, they plan to reveal them to the world at large.
These poor deluded souls say they're setting out to describe the way
the world looks to a cat. They're even muttering things about the
definitive cat book. From all I can gather, one of these hacks is a writer
of moderate talent, the other a so-called scientific journalist whose
competence requires further proof. Well, the first words for this piece
of effrontery that spring unbidden to my mind are ridiculous,
disgraceful, and totally deranged. Every human who looks into our
eyes and gets lost there, like someone hypnotised by a magician's
swinging pendulum, knows it isn't so much a case of our having a
secret, we are a secret. If you've fallen for a conjuring trick you can't
explain it: if you could, you wouldn't have fallen for it. Ignoring this
fact, however, these two megalomaniacs are attempting – in the
certainty of pitiful failure like their predecessors – to find a clear,
plausible explanation for the phenomenon of the cat. Just as if they
were dealing with the behavioural repertory of a nicely behaved dog.*

So what, I ask you, what about the metaphysics, the philosophy? What about analysis of the didactic interplay between fresh chicken livers and the existential digestion of all Being? What about that, then?

However, I have to admit that I do cast a glance at laboured expositions of this kind myself from time to time, just to keep up to date with the amazing nonsense human beings are always talking behind our backs. Over the course of time, in fact, I've become a positive connoisseur of the genre. It goes without saying that the writers of such alleged information books don't know the first thing about my kind. They generally employ most of their creative energy in copying from each other. And as with all copying, that leads to deviations from the truth. Tiny deviations, but taken all together they entirely distort or actually falsify the original. If anyone used this method to write an information book about human beings, it would represent its subjects copulating exclusively with certain makes of motor car and eating nothing but foods beginning with the curious syllable 'Mac'. We say those are very, very bad authors! And then there are the philosophers. I suppose that this species consists of recently divorced teachers who have taken a course in esotericism on Lanzarote, sitting in their heavily mortgaged and trendily styled homes, looking at their cats and getting a sudden flash of inspiration: the cat, the universe, the unpaid bill for reincarnation therapy! Or: I too was in Ancient Egypt! That sort are mad keen to see us as guides to their transcendent Disneylands, automatically assuming that our proper place is on a witch's hunched back and our real home is Nirvana. We say those are very, very dotty authors! Finally, I should mention the purely scientific if self-important experts. This sort likes to start by examining our excretions under an electron microscope, doing an instant chemical analysis of them, and then revealing the atomic constituents of the material, simply to tell the gentle reader what the cat ate. Just watching us eat isn't academic enough for these eggheads, and the books they write are correspondingly dry and lacking in any emotion. We say those are very, very boring authors!

We also say that human beings, with their ludicrous intelligence quotient, brainless nature and unpredictable relationship with our own kind are basically in no position to write anything sensible about Felidae, let alone anything important. Humans are and will remain pathetic creatures, creatures who can never sleep as comfortably, eat with as much pleasure or generally enjoy life as much as we can. Consequently, they can't write anything clever about us. QED.

Very well, then, back to the present book: it discriminates against the feline race; it claims to have solved a mystery, although the mystery itself vehemently disputes that fact; it tries desperately and unsuccessfully to turn myths into mathematics. What's it supposed to be good for? Nothing, obviously. Man proposes, Felis catus *disposes, you might say. However, let us be tolerant. Let us respect the right even of a couple of hacks suffering from delusions of grandeur to their freedom of opinion, even if their opinion of our literally divine race is worth about as much as that waste matter we ourselves bury as soon as we have produced it. But it does go against the grain to let this stuff be published without some criticism. I mean, in the first flush of reading it you might be tempted to accept these dreadful lies at face value. So I will take it upon myself to add a few comments, chapter by chapter, in the interests of damage limitation.*

Humans will never understand the cat and its mysterious nature. If they could, they would instantly commit hara-kiri in view of their own inadequacies. They must be content to contemplate our beauty, our elegance, and our intellectual achievements as measured in a fourth or feline dimension. Science and alchemy will get them nowhere.

Allow me to remind the authors of a truism: a wonder becomes no less wonderful if some clever fellow discovers that it functions with logical regularity. On the contrary, it's just proof of the wonder itself and the wonderful nature of our existence in this universe. But don't worry, it won't come to that. Obviously, the ultimate cat book could only be written by a cat, which may the goddess Bast forfend! Unlike human beings, we have been spared the scourge of exhibitionism. One way or another, there's nothing our two-legged friends can do but go on watching me and my kind to their heart's content. Be careful, though – because we are watching back.

Francis

A
Wild Animal
in the
Home

The psychological appeal of the cat

We shall never be able to say for certain whether the ancient Egyptians 'domesticated' the cat on purpose, or whether that cunning tiger on the hearth made its way with wise foresight, on velvet paws, into the homes of the subtle builders of the pyramids. Where there is a choice between truth and legend, we all know that people prefer the legend. In this case the stuff of which legends are made was contributed by a 'hard' scientist, Paul Leyhausen, a well-known expert on cat behaviour. Since the early civilisation of the Egyptians was frequently beset by famine, as indeed the Bible tells us, huge granaries had to be built to hold corn which would see people through the 'lean years'. Those signs of provident intelligence, however, also exercised magical powers of attraction on the intellectually less gifted

rats and mice. The devastation they were causing could not remain hidden for ever from the local African wild-cats. Somehow, something must have clicked in the brain of *Felis sylvestris lybica*. The prospect of free board and lodging, of being cared for and petted, induced the shrewdest members of the species to break with their origins, and they voluntarily exchanged the rigours of life in the wilderness for civilised pleasures. Leyhausen's view is that they took the Promethean step into 'self-domestication' of their own accord, the only other species to take that step being *Homo sapiens* when he decided to come down from the trees and put his money on civilisation. The rest is history. The Egyptians immediately took a liking to the mousers who had arrived on their doorsteps, declared them sacred and paid respectful homage to the animal now reborn as *Felis catus* – the common domestic cat.

This mythological account sounds convincing because it is so well suited to our self-willed domestic companion, the cat who will lie for hours on the radiator and walk away from the rodents it kills, scorning them in favour of various exotically flavoured tinned foods unknown to its ancestors. Moreover, cat owners, according to a survey conducted by a scientific institute, actually do have the impression that their small domestic lion made his way into their lives surreptitiously, almost unnoticed. The majority acquired a cat on the spur of the moment; over sixty per cent of the households questioned decided to add a furry member to the family on impulse, without planning it ahead. One day the cat just seemed to be there: such was the general tenor of their replies.

However, there are various arguments casting doubt on the

idea that it was the cat which first approached humans. For instance, the ancient Egyptians liked animals in general; they tamed and bred every species that came within their orbit, from monkeys to hyenas and crocodiles. The decorative wildcat can scarcely have escaped their enthusiastic attention. Then again, the brain volume of the cat decreased by about twenty-five per cent during its transition from the wild to domestication. This decrease is particularly marked in the cerebral cortex, where the highest intellectual gifts are situated. Wolves, incidentally, 'degenerated' even more as they became dogs. In any case, something must have gone wrong if the brainiest specimens were really the first to be tempted into an alliance with mankind.

Moreover, it is now thought very unlikely that the Egyptians fell for the cat's charm primarily because of its usefulness. In fact its hunting performance in general is probably commonly overestimated. Roger Tabor, the British cat expert, says that rodents in ancient Egypt usually seem to have been kept down by house-snakes. And the ancient Egyptians were already waging chemical warfare against voracious vermin over three thousand years ago. They used the sea onion or squill, a plant of the lily family, to kill Nile grass rats by inducing cardiac arrest in them. This form of rat poison is obviously so effective that it is sometimes used even today. The Egyptians' neighbours in Sumer preferred the mongoose, a speckled, silvery grey viverrid which is extremely alert but easy to tame. A Sumerian proverb ran: 'A cat for its thoughts, a mongoose for its deeds.' One cannot help thinking of that fabulous cat-like creature the Sphinx, whose enigmatic bearing suggests deep thought rather than animal instinct.

If man had not taken the cat to his heart for reasons more elevated than rat-catching, suggests the American animal behaviourist Roger A. Caras, he would hardly have agreed, over the centuries, to let it leave its post guarding his corn and move to a soft sofa by the fire instead. The bond between man and cat is something very special, since of all domestic animals (apart from cage birds and ornamental fish) the cat seems to be the least economically useful, and yet it has attained cult status. The cat brings no useful quarry home, does not guard our houses or drive unwanted intruders away. In the spirit of the saying about art for art's sake, however, it catches the eye, dazzling us with aesthetic pleasure. The cat has a well-proportioned, athletic body reminiscent of those sports cars made in wind tunnels by Italian designers who also have aesthetically pleasing names such as Colani and Fabrizi. Its graceful, smooth movement, the gliding curves of its body, its ability to speak with its limbs like a dancer, enchant our sense of harmony and proportion. In every civilisation that has produced art at all, artists have drawn and painted new variations on the subject of the cat. The greatest artistic minds in intellectual history have turned to the cat, not just for inspiration but out of pure delight in its beauty. These days interior decorators and glossy house-and-garden magazines have made the cat a symbol of gracious and comfortable living.

However, human influence on its breeding has added further pleasing refinements to the cat's chic and athletic appearance. Its genes have been manipulated to retain paedomorphic, i.e. child-like, features into adult life. This is primarily to do with the famous appeal of neoteny, the retention of infantile characteristics, which never fails to make itself felt in nature. It is a key stimulus consisting of a combination of those physical features which are typical of babies and make adults feel affectionate and protective. They include a head which is large in proportion to the body, big protruding eyes, bulging forehead, short muzzle, etc., and they are behind the design of cuddly toys. The cat's behaviour throughout its life also retains infantile features: its deep-seated playfulness, its purring, its never-ending demand for affection. The cat is the ideal baby surrogate, a Peter Pan who never grows up and provides constant satisfaction for our mothering instincts.

'The chief, the fundamental prime mover in man as in the animals is egotism, the urge to being and well-being ... Egotism, of its very nature, has no limits: man wishes to preserve his existence at all costs, wishes to keep it free at all costs from pain, including want and deprivation, wishes for the greatest possible amount of prosperity ... he wishes, if possible, to enjoy every pleasure ...'. These remarks dashed off by the great philosopher Arthur Schopenhauer contain some painful insights which do not go down very well today. 'Addiction' to the satisfaction of our own needs is more of a taboo subject in the modern social state than sexuality was in Victorian England. People display consideration for others, present themselves as social beings, make it appear, through their conduct, that their overweening egos are bowing to the good of the community. But deep inside us the untameable, animal drive for life burns on. Very likely that is where we get

our willingness to identify enjoyably with real or fictional figures who grab everything they can from life for the sake of ease and comfort.

Cats are an ideal screen upon which we can project these unbecoming desires. As solitary hunters who have never had to submit to the restraints of a rigid social order, they have the mentality of a hedonistic materialist. They have a positive genius for making themselves comfortable and commandeering the services of human 'tin-openers' to satisfy their own needs. They follow the self-interest principle with all the natural tyranny of a spoilt child. The cat takes it for granted that it has a right to life in a pleasant temperature, with a soft bed, a quiet background, and the assurance of a nicely varied diet: it demands these things sometimes seductively, sometimes indignantly, but always with a distinct air of being entitled to them. And when everything does go according to the cat's wishes, it will show its pleasure with positively indecent abandon. It is almost impossible not to feel some lurking admiration for this blatant pursuit of the pleasure principle. Yet the cat's life-style appears idle and frivolous to the busy, stressed human mind. Apart from their obsession with hunting mice (and tinned cat-food), cats are not exactly what a personnel manager would call ambitious. They prefer to 'hang out', lounge around on a soft bed, or get up to silly tricks. There is little danger of their ever contracting managerial stress diseases or stomach ulcers. If we were cats, Caras thinks, we would easily live to be a hundred and twenty-five and finally sleep ourselves comfortably to death.

A few morsels from the table of this *savoir-vivre*, of course, fall to us humans. With one of the most bewitching sounds in the world, its purr, the cat persuades us that it thinks we're wonderful. After all, we can always tell ourselves that such an animal has instincts and knows very well where it is bestowing its affections. It is as if unspoilt nature in person were complimenting us with flattering surges of sound. Being appreciated in that way is very welcome when you've been treated like dirt at work all day. Like cuddly little tigers, cats also enjoy rubbing their cheeks on your legs or rubbing faces with you, even when other people have made you feel like a social outcast. There are good reasons, in fact, for thinking that the real purpose of this affectionate gesture is for cats to mark us with their scent glands, labelling us as their property.

Because of this loving but in general not wholly unselfish way of caressing us, together with many other ambivalent features, the archetype of the 'eternal feminine' has long been projected on the cat. Perhaps Eve was made not from Adam's rib after all, as the Bible tells us, but from the tail of a cat. In the Christian world of the Middle Ages women were branded as lascivious, seductive creatures trying to drag the stronger sex down into the abyss with their baser instincts. This derogatory image was easily transferred to cats. They like physical closeness and love to be stroked and caressed. They are also incorrigibly flirtatious and unpredictable, and can change instantly from cuddly toy to spitting fury. The cat is equated with the dark and mysterious aspects of feminine sexuality in many proverbs and figures of speech. 'She purred like a cat' is the proud boast of men who crave recognition of their sexual prowess. The female cat, after all, lives a very promiscuous life, brazenly tempting several toms at once to love-play, but

she is perfidious too and will turn on her lover immediately after intercourse. The 'oldest profession in the world' has linguistic associations with feline attributes in many countries. A 'cat' is a colloquial term for a prostitute, operating from a 'cat-house', and 'pussy' is slang for the female genitalia or sexual intercourse, especially in American English.

In the past the cat has always been closer to women than the dog, man's hunting companion. Cats have been described as lustful, lazy, coaxing, inconstant and seductive. The supposed analogies go further. There are the cat's sharp claws, similar to fingernails, its light and restless sleep, its capricious nature, its fear of thunderstorms and love of comfort. 'In the cat I see woman with her ever-changing, sensitive soul,' said Casanova, who ought to have known. Woman and cat are both seen as creatures who, although domesticated, can never be entirely mastered. Both have physical charms which attract the admiring glances of those around them. Bast and Isis among the Ancient Egyptians, the Greek Demeter and the Celtic Ceridwen were all fertility goddesses in feline form. There is even a legend that when Jesus was born a cat was giving birth to her kittens in the same stable. In the thirteenth century, cats were the only pets nuns in English convents were allowed to keep.

The cat is surrounded by an aura of mystery already perceptible in the impassive features of the Sphinx. For the same reason, humans have sometimes accorded it devoted worship and sometimes hysterical persecution.

It is quite possible that the cat's psychological charm is largely to do with this intriguing sense of something 'different' in its nature. Man's proverbial best friend, the dog, will submit to almost any trainer, and is quite happy acting as the extension of a human arm. The cat remains a law unto itself, its strange wilfulness giving rise to endless speculations. It is in the nature of cats to go their own way. Before we ever knew the cat it lived the life of a solitary hunter, taking orders from no one. The sight of it allows us intimations of a life we cannot imagine, but which is as complex as our own although entirely different. It is the mark of a mature civilization to tolerate this difference without feeling it as a threat. According to the psychoanalyst Carl Jung, animals frequently reflect the unconscious and suppressed elements in the human psyche. The cat, combining the amenities of a domesticated animal with the freedom of its wild cousins, is a brilliant metaphor for the untamed, animal side of humanity visited by dim memories of its own distant origins. Domestication has only half succeeded with that purring bundle of fur at the fireside: the cat still has one foot planted in untouched nature. An uncanny change from amiable Dr Jekyll to savage Mr Hyde takes place as soon as it has gone out of the door; all the rules of civilisation and all the cat's paedomorphic aspects are eliminated, and the nature of a wild hunter imperiously takes over. The Janus mentality of the cat opens just a crack of the window through which, looking over the urban rooftops, we can glimpse our own original state.

Some people are more attuned to the cat's untamed character than others. In general, individuals obsessed by power seldom get on well with cats. Genghis Khan, Alexander the Great, Julius Caesar, Napoleon and Hitler were known as confirmed cat-haters. However, the cat is the ideal companion for those who would rather observe than rule.

Charles Darwin, Isaac Newton, Ernest Hemingway, Victor Hugo, Edgar Allan Poe, Doris Lessing and many other men and women of science and letters have all been cat-lovers. 'Artists like cats; soldiers like dogs,' is the way the British cat expert Desmond Morris sums it up.

The most striking evidence for this idea was provided by the Nazis. The leaders of the Third Reich lavished admiration on the dog (and the wolf), a kind of admiration which had similarities with the worship of the cat in ancient Egypt. At one of the Nazi party rallies a woman speaker even announced that she had conducted a conversation with a talking dog. When asked, 'Who is Adolf Hitler?' the animal, she claimed, had answered with doglike devotion, 'Adolf Hitler is my Führer.' An indignant Party member criticised this story as 'tasteless', but we are told by the American anthropologist Arnold Arluke that the speaker energetically defended herself. She pointed out that Hitler had introduced far-reaching measures for the protection of animals, and the good dog merely wanted to express its gratitude.

In fact the relationship of the Nazis to animals is one of the greatest paradoxes of history. Although they did unspeakably atrocious things to human beings, they showed surprising solicitude for animals. Directly after they seized power an extremely rigorous law on animal protection was rushed through, strictly regulating conditions of slaughter and imposing harsh penalties on vivisection and 'unnecessary' experiments on animals. Dogs, horses, monkeys and last but not least the domestic cat, were expressly marked out as 'particularly worthy of protection'. There were even provisos about the killing of crabs and lobsters in as humane a way as possible, and the leading thinkers of the National Socialist Party (who were often vegetarians) frequently and with much publicity racked their brains over the conservation and reintroduction of endangered species. This demented mixture of delusion, sadism and clear-sightedness is very well described in a historical outline by Arnold Arluke.

As mentioned above, women tend to have a greater affinity with cats while men are more likely to prefer dogs. This may well have something to do with the division of labour in the cave-man era, when men (and dogs) went hunting and thus developed community spirit, while women stayed in the camp, doing household tasks, and proved themselves indivi-dualists. Such tendencies, however, seem to have become much blurred by the social and historical developments of recent times. The results of the survey already quoted show that men feel almost as much of a personal link with the cat as women. The pleasure experienced in petting a cat, playing with it, etc., is almost equally felt by both sexes. According to Reinhold Bergler, professor of psychology at Bonn Univer-sity, in a study he himself carried out, people living alone, whether they are men or women, spend the same amount of time a day on average (sixty-five minutes) playing with their cats or stroking them. The results of a recent American survey showed that ninety per cent of all pet-owners regularly have 'conversations' with their pets; two-thirds give them Christ-mas presents; and about a third even leave the television on while they are out to provide entertainment.

The psychological *rapprochement* of the sexes and the fashion for cats (thirteen per cent of all German households keep a cat) probably go back to the same historical roots, described by sociologists as the quiet revolution or as post-materialism. The theory is that in the Western industrial nations, where all our most pressing material needs are satisfied, more and more people are concerned with 'higher' values such as self-development or environmental conservation. A more cynical view of the situation, however, would be that we are increasingly abandoning the values of duty in favour of those of pleasure. Be that as it may, both scenarios show a loss of respect for authority and of willingness to submit to it. By the same token, the tiger gains admittance to the sitting-room. Bergler's findings show that cat-owners are particularly appreciative of the following positive qualities in their pets: individuality, independence, an affectionate nature, playfulness, eroticism, originality, sincerity, straight-forwardness, intelligence, and ease of caring for the pet. It is noticeable that these cat-lovers regard themselves as having similar 'post-materialist' qualities. Compared to dog-owners, they consider themselves more emotional, fonder of physical contact, more generous, more tolerant and better balanced. Single people with cats feel lonely less often and believe they are less conventional. What they like best about the cat is its independence. They commented, again and again, that the cat 'isn't always bothering you'. While they often felt their partners were being 'disruptive', people almost never felt that cats were getting on their nerves. In fact there is a certain aristocratic dignity in the cat's attitude towards its human partner; the cat is almost never a 'nuisance' and is valued for its meticulous cleanliness, which means that its owner hardly has to do anything about its private body functions. And its second, wild nature gives it a high degree of independence, making it very unobtrusive and easy to look after. This view of the cat obviously fits in nicely with the uncommitted attitude of single people who would like such partners in human form. The character of Catwoman in the latest Batman film, a figure of unbridled sensuality, obviously reflects a collective piece of erotic wish fulfilment on the part of modern man. As usual, however, there is another side to the coin: our playful relationship with the cat will work properly only if we stick to the cat's rules. The cat behaviourist Dennis Turner, of Zürich, observed in the course of his studies that episodes of contact between human and cat last much longer if the animal takes the initiative and its human partner makes no great efforts to get close. One could say that those who want to take most from the relationship will eventually come off worst.

However, the cat is far more than a decorative accessory, an emotional stimulus or a philosophical symbol. Daily contact with cats is definitely good for their owners' health, bestowing advantages which are now being used in psychotherapeutic treatments. There are many indications that the mere sight of a relaxed cat is as infectious as the sight of another person yawning. It has been proved that stroking a favourite cat lowers blood pressure. On the other hand, blood pressure rises abruptly as you speak to another human, or even approach him or her with affectionate intent. Friendship with a familiar cat probably reinforces the immune system too, says Professor Bergler, thus increasing the expectation of life. Statistics show that people who have a loving relationship with a pet live longer than people wholly unconnected with the natural world. They do not fall ill so often, and if they do, then they have a less severe form of their illness. Roger Caras believes that this fact suggests a startling possibility. Perhaps the domestication process is exactly the opposite of what we have always thought. Cats may have 'bred' us especially to be cat-lovers who will live longer and healthier lives, and bring more cat-lovers into the world. After all, it is in the cat's own interests for the people who look after it to feel good and pass their attitudes on. If Caras is right, then the cat has actually been tinkering with our genetic inheritance since the time of the pyramids, manipulating us into the shape that best serves its needs.

Comments by Francis

Well, this is a fine start! Lies upon lies, half-truths, distortions. The moment human beings open their mouths to go boring on, saying things they think are clever about our history and our nature, all that comes out is a set of tall tales verging on outright insult. There are just too many old wives' tales here for me to consider it coincidence or ignorance. Just where am I to begin defending us? How am I to give the true picture while quivering inwardly with fury at such scientifically presented idiocy?

So we're supposed to have ingratiated ourselves with the ancient Egyptians because we preferred comfort to living in the wild. Oh, come on, wasn't it exactly the other way round? I mean, the sons of the desert didn't start being civilised until they took us into their huts, when, inspired by our high intellectual level, they soon rose to increasingly impressive cultural achievements. As far as I'm aware, the design of the pyramids derives straight from a sketch scribbled in the sand by the claws of a Libyan wildcat. Those two hacks skimped on the research work there. And they say the volume of our brains decreased by twenty-five per cent when we became domesticated. Now here, quite apart from the fact that I consider it a downright insult to regard our species as layabouts, I would like to draw your attention to the general law of miniaturisation. I'll grant you there was something imposing about the hi-fi monsters of the Bronze Age of electronics, with their valves and their huge loudspeakers. But what was the sound like? It came accompanied by nerve-racking crackling, while the stylus did a mischievous little jump whenever it reached a scratch, indelibly engraving certain lines of a song on one's youthful memory, and the bass could easily have been generated in a preserving jar. These days modern technology has done away with such drawbacks, while the technology itself has become Lilliputian. The miniature has triumphed over the inadequate colossus and has far outstripped its performance. Right, so it's the same with us and our brain size. As everyone knows, our intellect is greatly superior to that of mankind. Remember the saying that 'small is beautiful'? It applies in neurology too. Of course you're hardly going to think up these brilliant connections of cause and effect if you spend your time in badly aired rooms staring at computer monitors until your eyes are streaming and stacking up books and learned articles by assorted eggheads until the laboured dissertation on top of the pile falls off, making a devastating dent on your head and your powers of reasoning.

There's a lot in this book about the feline character too, and let me say at once that it's libellous. Words such as 'lazy' and 'egotistic', and the suggestion that we are anxious to maintain our supplies, occur far too frequently to be excused as the usual human tendency to get things wrong. No, slander has obviously been at work here, because the splendid qualities of my species most deserving of praise are those reduced ad absurdum *by typically human distortion. Lazy? To the*

outsider, the relaxed attitude of one of my kind, eyes closed or only half open, all four legs draped over the radiator, may indeed look like the ultimate in hedonism. But let me ask you, was the philosopher Kant, for instance, operating a metal punch tool at piece-work rates when he thought up all that stuff of his about the categorical imperative? Was Schopenhauer selling beefburgers in McDonalds when he plumbed the melancholy depths of our existence? Did Nietzsche go to the office at eight sharp every morning in order to compose his works? Okay, so pure philosophy is our trade, and although hidebound humans may regard us as lazy drones switching off from the world in orgiastic slumber, the fact is that we're really working away non-stop to solve the global problem. We'll let you know in good time when we've done it. So until then, Do Not Disturb.

Egotistic? Anxious to maintain supplies? Nonsense! We are merely and very touchingly demanding the rights of retired gods. Over the course of time human beings have attributed such infantile characteristics to the objects of their religious devotions that by now they resemble sexless, undemanding, tawdry icons of the Elvis variety. In the old days, however, there were gods who had both feet firmly planted on the ground. People sacrificed to them, even fed them. Without wishing to boast, I would like to point out that my kind came Number One in the divinities chart of early historical times, and certain later cults of the splinter group variety, such as Mariolatry, can be traced right back to those purring idols. Fertility, increased prosperity, good or bad fortune all depended directly on our goodwill. Surely it is only right and proper for gods, when pensioned off, to claim one, two or maybe three tins of food a day and a little attention in return for services rendered in the past? Wealth to the amount of whole national budgets is collected annually for invisible gods whose concrete achievements aren't subject to scrutiny by any audit office. So if ubiquitous deities who once decided the fate of kingdoms, and perhaps still do, require respect, affection, and a nice bit of fresh cod now and then from their former worshippers, I call it a wicked slander to put that down to self-interest.

CHAPTER 2

A
Lynx-eyed
View

Humans as seen by the cat

Cats have a consuming passion for watching human beings. Anyone who has ever known a cat will be familiar with its wide, inquisitive eyes as they follow the curious activities of its two-legged chef and provider. The lynx-eyed cat, observing the vanity of human wishes and human conduct from ground level, features in countless pictures, from Stone Age scenes showing magical practices to the present day. Since the eyes of the cat are not at the side of its head, like those of the dog and the horse, it can focus both eyes at once on objects and give us a full frontal stare. It is unlikely that the cat 'went over' to the ancient Egyptians without making thorough observations first. One can imagine it lurking safe in cover while taking a good look at the strange and fascinating conduct (and strange gait) of the proud people of the Nile. It would be cynical to read nothing but a vulgar desire for luxury accommodation into the decisive step it then took. The cat, with its quick intelligence, must have suspected for some time that there was something more exciting, varied, attractive and entertaining in the lives of those huge and strange creatures than the dreary round of catching mice. Although we humans no longer build pyramids or wrap mummies in bandages, we still do countless things every day to arouse a cat's curiosity. We set all kinds of strange machines and devices working, and they in turn produce surprising pictures, sounds, and even things to eat. Our clumsy and inelegant way of moving around, not much of an advance on the days of ancient Egypt, is a whole chapter to itself, obliging the cat to take constant care not to get trodden on by some giant weighing twenty times as much as it does. We are always going from one room into another and opening and closing doors, our most annoying invention. Humans have strange habits, like actually getting into a tub of water of their own free will, and the place where we perform our private functions must appear ridiculous to the user of a litter tray. Finally, cats must certainly envy our cultural achievements: not just reading and writing but most important of all, the knack of opening tins.

The voyeuristic tendencies of the cat are assisted by its excellent vision, and consequently the firm of Kodak used the cat's eyes as the theme of an advertising campaign. The British veterinary surgeon Bruce Fogle tells us how the United States Army even tried using cats on leads to guide their soldiers through the jungle by night. This unlikely-sounding project eventually had to be abandoned because the animals, magical as their eyes might be, were far from willing to be recruited as guide cats for disorientated GIs. A confidential report recorded that one squad was led off to all points of the compass by its feline pilots when ordered to move out. The cats kept leading the humans at the other end of their harnesses into bushes and jungle brushwood because of their irresistible impulse to chase mice and birds, and their natural playfulness made them keep stalking and attacking the pack straps dangling from the backs of the soldiers ahead of them. If the weather was bad or even looked like turning bad, the feline draft-dodgers were nowhere to be found.

This was not in fact the first attempt to use the cat's legendary eyesight for purposes of modern warfare. During the Second World War, British RAF pilots often had great difficulty identifying enemy aircraft in the dark at night. In 1941 a suggestion was actually put forward that a cat should be part of the crew of every RAF fighter plane. The idea was to aim the guns the way the cat was staring and then fire them. Unfortunately we are not told if this notion was ever tried out in practice. Many centuries earlier, in 525 BC, the Persian king Cambyses is said to have turned the ancient Egyptians' worship of cats to account as a warlike ruse when he was trying to capture the city of Pelusium, which was supposed to be impregnable. If the legend is true, his warriors stormed the city carrying cats on their shields, thus causing its inhabitants to surrender without a fight out of religious awe. However, there is no indication that the cats would actually have allowed themselves to be misused in this shameful way without putting up resistance.

On the whole it is rather unlikely that such a recalcitrant

loner as the cat could ever be usefully recruited into army service; it would need the heart of a dog in its supple feline body. Of all cat species, only lions, with their doglike pack mentality, might be suitable for paramilitary operations. According to biblical legends, lions guarded the Ark when desperate humans were trying to make their way into its safe refuge. In this story, the king of the beasts features not as a commander but as a military policeman ensuring the smooth running of the operation. Both Roman emperors and certain high-ranking Nazis kept tame lions as a status symbol, but also for their personal protection.

The cat, a miniature tiger stalking prey in the dark, has inherited its built-in night-sight device from its large cousins. The cat's eyes are large in proportion to its relatively small skull. Human eyes would be the size of bowling balls if they were designed on the same proportional scale as the cat's. Round eyes like marbles looking straight ahead of it, and often compared with the eyes of a woman, give the cat its typical charismatic look of alertness, which is also reminiscent of a primate at the baby stage.

The most astonishing achievement of the cat's eye is its extraordinarily high sensitivity to light. The American veterinarian Michael W. Fox has described experiments in which cats were trained to look for their food in the dark behind two wooden screens. One screen was dark, the other illuminated by a tiny amount of light, but it still hid the food behind it. The cats went straight to the right place even when the amount of light was six times less than humans would need to do the same. Even a spark of starlight is enough for the cat to pick up the revealing movement that betrays the whereabouts of a mouse; in the same conditions a human could not see his hand before his face. The reason is that the eyes of the cat are equipped with a highly efficient means of enhancing residual light. The counterpart to the light-sensitive film in a camera is the retina of the eye. It consists of several layers of specialised nerve cells or receptors to pick up rays of light and turn them into nerve impulses, which are then transmitted to the brain.

However, the cat's eye contains a mirror-like structure described by anatomists as the *tapetum lucidum*. It consists of ten to twenty layers of highly reflective zinc and certain proteins, especially vitamin B (riboflavin). The tapetum throws back those rays of light which were not absorbed by the retina when they first entered the eye. This gives the retina additional stimulation, which in turn massively increases the eye's ability to see in poor light. This magnificent piece of natural technology increases light intake by almost fifty per cent.

But the clever dodge whereby the feline tapetum is thickly plastered with riboflavin and zinc gives it an additional and remarkable quality: it is fluorescent. That means that it reinforces short-wave light, which is invisible to the eye, and transfers it to a higher wave-length situated in the visible spectrum. The cat's tapetum is thus responsible for the mysterious way its eyes glow in the dark when illuminated by an artificial source of light such as car headlights. This principle was detected, with great perspicacity, by an Italian doctor called Giovanni Raiberti, who published a survey of the cat's physiology written in ironic style in the year 1845. He accounts for the mystery of the shining layer by saying that 'it gathers together the weakest rays of light, those which the

human eye cannot pick up, into a focal point and reflects them from the back of the eye, thus radiating that terrifying light which instantly makes the blood freeze in its victims' veins'.

The principle upon which the tapetum is constructed also makes it clear that evolution, that brilliant builder, and human technology often resort to the same idea. The metal zinc was already being used to make mirrors in ancient China because of its reflective qualities, and fluorescent combinations of zinc and other materials are frequently used as a luminous layer, for instance in the picture tubes of television sets. However, the 'cat's eyes' at the back of a bicycle or set down the middle of the road lag far behind the abilities of their animal model. Reflectors of this kind merely consist of quantities of pyramid-shaped fragments which break up the light countless times and then beam it back the way it came; this has nothing to do with the phenomenon of fluorescence.

Humans have no such little reflective mirrors at the back of the eye; it would save hunters a good deal of high-tech equipment if they did. In photographs taken with a flash human eyes often look red. This effect is caused by the many blood vessels in front of and behind the retina. We can, in fact, develop what is called an amaurotic cat's eye, but it is a very unpleasant disease of the eye which causes blindness and shows itself in a yellowish, reflective pupil. The cause of this cat-like light reflex is a tumour called a retinoblastoma, which grows into the vitreous body of the eye and detaches the retina.

Many other nocturnal animals besides the cat are equipped with a tapetum. Even the dog has a similar reflective surface in the eye, but its molecular structure is nowhere near as refined and regular as the cat's, according to the Canadian anatomist Charlie R. Braekevelt. In many fish this reflective film consists of a layer of the same microscopically tiny crystal grains as are responsible for the silvery gleam of their scales. The colour of the resulting 'eyeshine' depends on the coloration of the photopigments in the retina. All species of cat, like deep sea fish, produce a shining greenish gold reflection. If a tiger is caught in the beam of a searchlight by night, its eyes glow with a wonderful golden green, celebrated by the poet Blake in his famous poem: 'Tyger, tyger, burning bright, / In the forests of the night ...' The French poet Baudelaire also paid poetic tribute to the cat's glowing eyes: *'Le feu de ses prunelles pâles, / Clairs fanaux, vivantes opales'.* ('The fire of its pale pupils, / Bright lanterns, living opals'.) Hares and rabbits reflect back a red glow, while the eye of the antelope produces a plain white reflection.

The magic glow in the eyes of the cat was arousing all kinds of metaphysical speculation as long ago as the days of ancient Egypt. Ancient Egyptian society as a whole was obsessively constructed around the idea of life after death. Death, in the land of the Pharaohs, meant what space probes and microchips mean to us. The entire structure of Egyptian civilisation, with its pyramids, its tombs, its mummies – and its cats – was seen as a means of communication with the other world. The Egyptians thought that the cat, too, had a special line to the world beyond. They believed, for instance, that the sun they worshipped was still reflected in its eyes long after the sun had vanished from human sight. They took the cat's eye as their model for the design of the hieroglyphic *ru*, which originally denoted 'birth' and 'transition'. In occult lore, this symbol was made mystical and stood for every form of metamorphosis and for a gateway into another world. A distant echo of the hieroglyphic *ru* is found today in the symbol denoting the female sex, which is reminiscent of a mirror with a cross-shaped handle, and relates to the goddess Venus.

The witch-hunters of the Middle Ages, however, thought the glow of the cat's eyes reflected hell-fire, connected it with uncanny powers and black magic, and threw cats on the pyres where they had already burned women accused of witchcraft. At this time, too, the deluded notion that witches could easily slip into the shape of a black cat to go about their nefarious business undisturbed gained currency. This metamorphosis, in its own turn, has remarkable similarities with the legend of the vampire who can disguise himself in the shape of a bat.

In past centuries, many black Americans had a superstitious belief that cats could see ghosts – and were reflecting part of the ghostly sights they had seen back into our world. Consequently they often sacrificed cats ceremonially and misused them for various magic voodoo rituals. In early modern times, finally, when the study of natural sciences began to make headway, the phenomenon was explained by the supposed presence of phosphorus in the cat's eyes, lighting the animal's path on its nocturnal roamings. In antiquity, people were firmly convinced that the lynx, a close relative of the cat, could see through stone walls in pitch darkness. The ability of the big cats to see at night almost cost the animal tamer Clyde Beatty his life, as he describes in his autobiography. He was just demonstrating his skills in a cage full of lions and tigers when a technical defect put out the circus lights. This was no problem for the animals, who could see well enough by the remaining residual light, but Beatty was unable to see a thing. He knew that he must on no account let the animals become aware of his sudden blindness; if they had guessed at his handicap they would have attacked him at once. He instinctively realized that he must not deviate in the least from the usual sequence, so as not to arouse their suspicions. Somehow or other, he proceeded with the usual show, guided only by feel and experience. This ruse did in fact deceive the animals and save his life; but for his understanding of the world of the feline senses the story would certainly have had a different ending.

By comparison with the human eye, the eye of the cat is more curved and the lens tilted further to the interior. This gives it a relatively wide angle of vision, and the picture which falls on the retina is five times brighter to start with than in humans. Cats also perceive ultra-violet radiation and other wavelengths which bypass the human eye. However, they cannot see the infra-red area which many natural scientists (and hunters) spy on with their night-sight devices. One of the most surprising discoveries about the cat's vision was made by the American scientist Frank Morell when he found nerve cells or neurones in the cat's brain which are responsible for the processing of optical impressions. Many of these sight neurones were activated even when the cat was put in a dark room and heard certain sounds. Feline brain cells, familiar as they are with the different modalities of sense, are probably often interchangeable and can take over for cells with different specialisations. We know that in humans blind from birth certain optical areas of the brain are converted into aural centres. In cats, however, it seems that information can switch from one channel (hearing) to another processing track (sight), performing an action scientifically described as synaesthesia. Synaesthesia is the amalgamation of different sensory channels which usually function quite separately. Sounds are perceived as images, while smells are 'felt' as a gentle touch. Most of us, after all, can make sense of expressions such as 'loud' or 'clashing' colours, or 'colourful' sounds. There are already popular computer programmes into which you can feed songs or concertos and see the musical vibrations transformed into shimmering visual structures. Synaesthesia is frequently found in literature in the form of metaphorical descriptions of feelings that are difficult to define precisely. The poets of the Romantic period were particularly fond of synaesthesia; they also tended to like cats, and produced several immortal works of feline literature, in particular the delightful fairy tale of *Puss in Boots* and E. T. A. Hoffmann's *The Philosophy of Life of Murr the Cat*. The Romantics, consumed by a sense of unquenchable longing and using poetry to cast a spell of enchantment over everyday life, used the stylistic device of synaesthesia to reveal hidden connections and to cross frontiers of meaning.

However, evolution can hardly have created synaesthetic nerve cells just so that the cat could reel intoxicated about the place in a state of poetic rapture. The task of such related perceptions is probably to give the cat more precise information about the outside world, presenting it to the mind's eye as a complete and fully dimensional work of art. Cats are supposed to have astonishing abilities to find their way home unerringly even over incredible distances. Perhaps they really do have a synaesthetic aural image of the sounds of home stored in the memory, and make their way towards that image step by step. One hardly likes to surmise what visions a cat may have on hearing a loud hiccup or even a symphony by Mahler.

In line with the requirements of a good hunter, the fields of vision of a cat's two eyes overlap to a considerable extent, providing a kind of stereoscopic vision in 3-D which also takes account of depth and distance. The brain is thus fed twice over with information about the same section of an image, from two slightly different perspectives, and converts the difference between these two impressions into a three-dimensional experience. The cat's dual system extends over an angle of about a hundred and thirty degrees, directed straight forwards. Besides this binocular (two-eyed) field of vision, the cat also has a monocular or one-eyed field. This peripheral vision, almost eighty degrees on each side, provides only two-dimensional perception without any depth. The remaining area around the cat, amounting to about two-ninths of a circle, is out of its sight. This invisible area is centred exactly on the cat's tail. The human field of vision covers two hundred and ten degrees, i.e. about seventy-five degrees less than the cat's, and we can take in a hundred and twenty degrees of this area with both eyes.

Only a hunter who need not fear enemies can keep his vision directed straight ahead, where the action is. Such a narrow angle would be much too dangerous for a prey animal, since greedy mouths might well be coming up behind it. Creatures like mice and rabbits, which are generally the hunted rather than the hunters, therefore have all-round panoramic vision without any depth of focus, strongly concentrated on movement. On the extreme borders of their field of vision, however, both cats and humans share with their prey a two-dimensional flat optic area. This drew from the French cat expert Jean-Louis Hue a poetic remark which could also be applied to human hunters and collectors: 'The cat is thus playing a double game: at the centre it has the vision of a beast of prey, on both sides the vision of the victim. The lion and the gazelle are both present in its eye.'

However, some creatures which must change swiftly from hunter to hunted and back again take this puzzle even further. The chameleon, for instance, can turn each of its two eyes sideways independently of the other. Once on the track of prey, the hunter directs both eyes forward so that their fields of vision overlap stereoscopically. In this way its tongue can unerringly snap up a fly passing in blissful ignorance. Back in the role of prey, it turns its eyes defensively to the side again. The chameleon literally has eyes everywhere. Incidentally, it is thought that the cat's field of vision may have become larger since it was domesticated, and has thus lost some of its 3-D abilities. If so, this would be a fascinating instance of evolution. Since the tamed marauder hardly has to bother about hunting rodents to survive these days, it has gradually become able to allow itself the luxury of an enlarged optic angle. After all, you do not need any particular depth of focus to murder a tin of cat-food.

Despite the refinement of their visual apparatus, cats are rather worse at estimating distance than humans. One reason for this is that humans compensate for their rather restricted field of vision by more, and more extensive, eye movements, made possible by certain special features in the mechanical construction of the lens. Moreover, the cat's head is simply smaller than ours. The eyes are closer together, the two sections of an image received by the brain are more similar, and they thus contain less information about depth. However, the cat makes up for this inbuilt structural deficiency by practising a manoeuvre which every cat owner will have observed. At a critical point, when precise information about distance is necessary, for instance when stalking or just before pouncing, the animal begins rhythmically swinging its head in an arc, from left to right. The manoeuvre is reminiscent of the way blind people will sometimes swing their heads rhythmically when excited – or perhaps, like Stevie Wonder, performing a song with much emotion. It allows the cat's brain to absorb more data about depth. The closer the cat comes to the mouse (or its food bowl), the greater is this optical deepening of the impression it receives. Even one-eyed cats can create an impression of space for themselves, but to do so they have to swing their proud heads in a wide, exaggerated movement like that of a pendulum, which to other cats makes them look slightly deranged. Cats seem to take their precise perception of space for granted: hence the surprise a cat shows when for once its pounce misses the mark.

Although cats have eyes considerably more sensitive than those of humans, their actual sharpness of vision is less than ours. This is to do with the structure of the cat's retina, where nature has concentrated on sensitivity to light at the expense

CAT SENSE

of sharp vision. Every amateur photographer will know the principle: light-sensitive films always have a lower power of resolution, and the finished picture has coarser graining.

There are two kinds of photo-receptors in the mammalian retina: rods, which are very sensitive to light, and cones, which provide sharpness and colour vision. The cones, which perform only in good light, are particularly densely situated in a special pit or depression in the centre of the retina, the fovea, also called the 'yellow spot' because of its pigmentation. This area of concentration is the only one to lack the nerves and blood vessels which overrun the receptors in the rest of the retina and slightly cloud vision. In the fovea, moreover, every single cone is joined to a nerve cell of its own, while several cones have to share a nerve cell in the peripheral areas. This means that neuronal resolution is lower on the periphery.

In humans, the fovea is always arranged in circular form, and as we read the fovea focuses on only a few printed letters at a time. The brain gets a sharp impression from this visual point alone, while everything around is blurred. The cat's eye is very different: its fovea is directed horizontally, out sideways. In big cats like the cheetah, the evolutionary architect has taken this structure to extremes: cheetahs have a yellow spot which is actually shaped like a horizontal line. Cats are therefore extremely quick to see prey moving across the screen on the horizon, while they have more difficulty focusing on small objects (like printed letters). However, prey animals too have entered into the competitive spirit of an arms race. Gazelles, for instance, have a long, horizontal fovea with which they can scan the landscape for dangers.

When the cat becomes aware of something like a mouse among the bushes, it uses the 'sharp spot' in the centre of the retina to take a good look. Many cells in the cat's retina are constructed so as to act as movement detectors, and they immediately raise the alarm if so much as an ant changes position. Frogs are equipped with similar movement detectors. They are programmed from birth to pick up the flies which form the main part of the frog's diet. This special equipment means that the cat does not have to explore the length and breadth of any suspect territory. It has only to move its head briefly to pick up give-away vibrations.

Cats often sit or lie about with an expression that may strike us as stupid or vacant. The reason is probably the relative fuzziness of the image at the centre of their angle of vision. However, the moment some stimulus touches the edge of their field of vision, in particular something making jerky or quivering movements, the hunter comes wide awake. Movement of any kind takes absolute priority for the cat, but some movements are much more stimulating than others. Objects the right size to be pounced on and moving away from the cat are absolutely irresistible. Something merely gliding past on the edge of the field of vision is very interesting too, but will not infallibly make the cat move.

Because of the cat's dynamic reaction to movement, mice and other prey animals have a habit of standing perfectly still, as if rooted to the spot, when they think something may be wrong, and keeping literally 'quiet as a mouse'. The protective reflex of going rigid with fear, built into the instinctive repertory of animals which figure prominently on the menu of other animals, is described by behavioural scientists as

'freezing'. 'Frozen' creatures, although motionless, are pumped full of adrenalin and have an enhanced power of perception, so that in an emergency they can switch rapidly into gear and react with fight or flight. Freezing is not the same as the playing-dead reflex; it is simply that frozen mice have a better chance of not being picked up by the movement detector in the cat's eye. The cat's vision is best in a zone between two and six metres away from it, where it can practically see the grass growing. In the area closest to it, however, the cat's excellent sight lets it down; its vision could be said to lack a macro-lens. This accounts for certain clumsy manoeuvres: for instance, if a cat's bowl is very close it may grope its way towards it like a zombie.

We shall probably never be sure whether a cat is really admiring our new mauve curtains, or averting its eyes from a T-shirt in glaring colours. For a long time scientists were sure that the cat saw its nine lives as a black-and-white film because it had no colour vision: not so much a matter of all cats looking grey at night as of all cats *seeing* grey at night. As mentioned above, the proportion of the cones responsible for colour vision in the cat's retina is smaller than in *Homo sapiens*. If cats are trained long enough they can in fact tell certain colours apart, but only if the coloured object occupies a large part of their field of vision. The closer the cat comes to the colourful stimulus, the better its ability to distinguish colour.

In recent years, receptors have been found in the cat's magic eye which are sensitive to green and blue, but no sensors which pick up red. To date, experiments have shown that after a while cats can tell red and blue apart, and can distinguish them from white, while green, yellow and white are indistinguishable to them. They see red as a kind of mid-grey. All in all, colours which seem bright and glaring to us show cats, at most, the quiet tones of a picture in pastel shades. The American biologist Sandra Sinclair concludes that a cat walking through a lush green meadow and passing a bush of blood-red roses probably sees only a pale background and a pale bush with flowers of some dark shade. The idea is rather reminiscent of the experience of a patient of the famous neurologist Oliver Sacks, who survived a car accident but suffered brain damage which left him unable to recognise colours. Human skin appeared to him 'rat-coloured', and food without any colour struck him as disgusting and inedible. We ought to point out that cats consider items coloured like rats, or indeed like mice, delicious and very edible indeed.

Like most living creatures with highly developed perception of colour, human beings have cones with not just two but three different photopigments. One is principally receptive to blue light, another to green and the third to yellowish green. The fact that two of the three pigments in *Homo sapiens* react to green indicates that they developed at a period when our ancestors were living in tropical forests where the colour green (produced by chlorophyll) was predominant. The brain receives information from the three types of cones, mingles them and thus produces a multi-coloured picture with a broad palette of shades. Humans have developed colour vision because their forebears had eyes which had to keep a careful watch on the ripening of edible fruits, and notice which animals and plants (often brightly coloured) were better avoided.

The American brain scientist Robert W. Williams recently discovered that at birth domestic cats have a sophisticated although only latent aptitude for 'real' colour vision. The Spanish wild-cat, which hunts in the bright mid-day sun, like many other small wild relatives of our pets (and the cheetah), has two or three times as many cones in the slit of its eye as the domestic cat, and is thus presumably fully able to see colour. The domestic cat, whose ancestors once had to go hunting for food by night near human settlements, also still possesses the equipment for seeing in full colour at the beginning of its life, but the ability is soon cancelled out by genetic programming because the cat has no use for it. Cats have probably retained this ancestral relic of their history to the present day because it could be useful if they ever had to return to their original life-style.

The British cat expert David Taylor suspects that in normal circumstances the cat's eye recognises colour, but the brain does not assess it: in effect, the eye knows things that the brain does not, the reason being that bright colours are no use in hunting grey mice. Roger Caras suspects that cats may not see the same glorious range of colour as a human admiring an exhibition in an art gallery or a meadow of wild flowers, but that they perceive as much colour as they need for survival in their own ecological niche. Tigers, in any case, react strongly to colours; for instance, their keepers only have to freshen up the paint on a toy whose attractions have worn off, and a tiger's urge to play with it will revive. Lethargic tigers apparently stupefied by the sun will instantly be wide awake if a human keeper wearing a brightly coloured T-shirt comes into sight.

Even if colours look much paler to cats than to us, they can regulate the amount of light entering their sensitive eyes much faster and more precisely than we can. This is important to a nocturnal hunter who is also active in bright daylight. Everyone has experienced the painful moment of emerging from a darkened cinema into glaring sunlight, and we all know how long it takes for the eye to penetrate blackness on entering a dark room. In bright light the cat narrows its pupils to a vertical slit and not, as in humans (and the cameras they construct), to a smaller circle. This sliding-door mechanism means that light intake can be almost entirely suspended, whereas the round aperture of the human eye only half closes. Beasts of prey frequently have vertical pupils, since they have to see their quarry a long way off, while sheep, goats and other potential victims are equipped with horizontal pupils; they have to be alert to what is going on beside them too.

In addition, cats can decrease the amount of light they take in by lowering their lids to make the eye itself a horizontal slit. If conditions then get darker, the whole mechanism works in reverse. These two slits at right angles to each other provide the cat with an extremely precise and quick means of adjustment. The connection with hunting mice at night is obvious. The lion, which kills its prey in bright daylight, contracts its pupils to round pinheads. Moreover, this aperture-control mechanism conveys meaning in the cat's body language, as Leyhausen discovered years ago. A cat lying in wait or beginning to attack has contracted pupils, but if the cat is angry or frightened, the pupils expand under the influence of a surge of adrenalin. A cat blinking at us or

closing its eyes is expressing trust and showing that it feels friendly.

The eyes are described as the mirror of the soul in humans, and in cats too they are very closely allied to the seat of intelligence and intellectual gifts. Even the eyes of tiny kittens just taking their first tottering steps out of the nest are learning by observation, in order to develop good hunting skills. Their tireless teacher, the mother cat, will bring her playful offspring a few slightly injured mice as specimens for inspection, rather like a lecturer presenting a class of medical students with a suitable subject for theoretical study. At first, if the specimen attempts to leave the lecture theatre without permission, the mother cat herself will kill it. After a while, however, she will simply sketch a movement towards the would-be runaway, who is then swiftly finished off by her eager students. Basic hunting skills are of course instinctive to the cat, but it obviously takes the ritual described above to add the finishing touches. We can tell that from comparing kittens who have learnt to hunt mice from their mother and those who have not. Small hunters who have practised under maternal supervision are more successful at catching prey later. There are two main reasons for that: they have made a much closer study of their prey, and they have had more practice in delivering the efficient neck-bite which kills the cat's victim.

Learning by observation is regarded by psychologists as one of the highest and most complex ways of acquiring knowledge. The reason is that in the process of imitation, a number of very ingenious patterns are being studied all at once; in simpler forms of learning, on the other hand, the lesson contains far less information. Consequently, the participants go through the entire procedure in the proper order, even though it sometimes entails a great deal of trouble. A good example is the mother cheetah who keeps bringing her cubs young hares. The cubs will catch only forty-five per cent of all the hares who take to their heels during the lesson; the mother cheetah herself could easily kill twice as many. However, she will not deprive her young of valuable experience, even if the whole family must pay for it with empty stomachs at the end of the day, as the American biologist T. M. Caro points out.

Cat books always suggest that the miniature lions which are our domestic cats regard their human companions as outsize mother figures all their lives – little as we generally resemble the ancient Egyptian goddess Bast, whose human torso bears the elegant head of a member of the Felidae family. However, we do 'spoil' cats with petting and affectionate personal contact, making them revert pleasurably to a phase of their lives when they were cleaned and tended by the mother cat's rough tongue. The cat on your lap sometimes performs a stamping, massaging movement with its forepaws; this treading or 'kneading' is a return to infancy, when it had the effect of stimulating the mother's milk glands.

For several thousand years, the cat has been viewing humans with unending curiosity, and we cannot really form an accurate idea of what its X-ray eyes actually see. Our skin is not brightly coloured, and as we have neither fur nor feathers, there is only our clothing to stimulate colour perception. Nor do we provide much stimulus for the movement detector in the cat's eye. Not many of us can 'moon-walk' weightlessly over the stage of real life, like Michael Jackson or the dancers in the musical *Cats*. As a rule, however, our activities do not entail those sudden, abrupt, 'mouse-like' movements which excite a cat. Sometimes we do things which attract the cat's concentrated attention: knitting, for instance, or cutting and tying string. Our hands or feet can sometimes seem independent, making suspect movements which stimulate the cat's nerves and its hunting instinct. Cats whose mouths water at the sight of delicious prey such as a small bird will sometimes begin to 'chatter' at it amid signs of great excitement; this strange sound is a 'vacuum activity', a substitute for the killing bite which the excited hunter would like to deliver. However, says Caras, it is unthinkable that cats would ever display this behaviour at the sight of a human being: we may be bitable, but we are not edible.

One of the strangest products of human civilisation, the television set, is simply a flickering display of light to the cat. As we all probably remember from our schooldays, the film moves because individual pictures succeed each other so rapidly that they merge together and the eye perceives them as a movie. In the language of technology this means that the sequence of pictures is above the 'flicker fusion frequency'. This measurement for the temporal resolution power of the eye, as the British biologist John Bradshaw tells us, is twice as high in cats as in humans. They are therefore still seeing separate, independent pictures where the human eye sees everything as a moving whole. The cat's flicker fusion frequency is 60 hertz, whereas the TV screen shows only fifty changes of picture per second. So if the cat wants a real viewing of a Disney cartoon, for instance, it must wait for the advent of High Density Television or HDTV, which will suit its own visual abilities. Many fluorescent lights also flicker at what to the human eye is the invisible frequency of 50 hertz. It is possible that the cat sees not just the flashes of light but also the dark phases in between them, so that its visual impression is something like that of strobe lighting in a disco. For structural reasons, however, the cat has to pay a price, although not too high a one, for its rapidity of perception: very slow movements, which the human eye can just perceive, are outside the scope of the cat's vision.

However, the cat's rapid flicker fusion frequency is by no means the fastest in the animal kingdom. The light receptors of our unwelcome domestic companion the housefly can keep up to three hundred separate pictures a second apart. This ability helps the little stunt flier to keep its eye on details rushing by underneath it, despite its own high speed. Since the fly registers such short intervals of time, it can react to a hand coming out to swat it in less than a hundredth of a second. Our clumsy gestures must strike it as pitiful attacks carried out in slow motion.

Getting along with humans is usually easier for a cat and causes fewer problems than encounters with members of its own species, not counting its mother. This is to do with the life-style of a solitary hunter to whom its own kind always means competition for food and sex. Carnivores who hunt prey can never afford to have such a relaxed relationship with their neighbours as cows grazing in a meadow. They would agree with Sartre, who wrote of his fellow men: 'The Other is in principle the one who is watching me, the latent death of my own opportunities.' And even more harshly, 'Hell is other people.' A cat acting as if it simply did not see another cat is only putting on a show. However, even the fixed, unwavering stare of a human being can infuriate a cat. In feline body language, staring with eyes wide open is an aggressive challenge. We should satisfy our desire to look at a cat when the cat itself is looking away, suggests Desmond Morris. According to his theory, this explains why cats sometimes make straight for people who dislike them: these cat-haters look firmly away, intentionally remaining very still and keeping their voices low, with the idea, as one might say, of letting sleeping cats lie. Cat-lovers, on the other hand, allow their enthusiasm to overcome them and do exactly the opposite. Consequently the cat prefers the person speaking a reserved, well-behaved body language.

Incidentally, cats are perfectly well able to recognise familiar people from their appearance, even at a distance of a hundred metres. However, they do not identify a person by facial characteristics but by general body outline, and in particular by that person's typical movements. This is something which has its parallels in human memory. Memories of static, fixed details are usually very vague, while moving, dynamic features and events stick in the mind far better. For instance, experiments have shown that subjects had no difficulty in recognising a familiar person when moving in complete darkness and shown up by points of light. However, if the person just stood still identification was impossible. The mammalian perceptive system has obviously evolved along lines of action and 'drive'.

As many remarkable stories and legends show, there has never been any lack of attempts to transfer the cat's highly developed vision to the human sensory system. A story from ancient China tells of a peasant who had an incurably diseased eye replaced by the eye of a cat. The operation was successful, and the patient acquired the fantastically visual acuity of a member of the Felidae family. But there turned out to be complications: he could not close his new eye at night because it was always looking out for rats. Something that was once only a legend sends a shiver down the back as one thinks of the latest newspaper reports of transplant operations, in which hearts, livers and other internal organs are already being implanted into human patients as spare parts.

A remedy for loss of vision taken from a medical manual of 1639 sounds similarly macabre. It tells the reader to take the head of a black cat, burn it to ashes, and sprinkle the affected eye with the ashes three times a day. In the climate of thought of the time, the cat's black colour probably symbolised the darkness surrounding the head of the patient to be treated. Cats and the sense of sight were so closely connected in the Middle Ages that a legendary ointment supposed to make you invisible had cat's fat as its basic ingredient. It was in particular demand among thieves wishing to go about their nefarious business in the perfect disguise of invisibility. The idea at the back of people's minds was probably that something with sharp sight when alive would confer total loss of visibility when dead.

The cat watches us with constant fascination, as if expecting some miracle at any moment, even some dawning of enlightenment, much as human beings will speculate on mysterious 'encounters of the third kind' with extra-terrestrial beings. Even the ancient Egyptians believed that the cat had

secret links with the other world. Perhaps the cat thinks that its two-legged super-mother knows the way to the eternal hunting grounds.

Comments by Francis

Well, not so bad after all. I must admit to feeling a certain pride as I read certain passages of the account of our wonderful eyes given above. However – trust humans – they are telling only half the truth. In fact they ignore the most important point of all, presumably to exalt themselves above other species even in their weakest sphere. I will pass over the suggestion that we have poorly developed colour vision without further comment. I mean, what's so great about colour anyway? Does it do anything much to enrich optical experience? Just compare a black-and-white forties film with one of today's stupid colour movies. You can watch the masterpieces of the golden age of cinema, created only with light, shade and sheer magic, and feel as much enjoyment at the eighteenth viewing as the first, but one of those gaudy modern jobs is usually just irritating, and somehow you seem to forget it straight afterwards. And isn't a charcoal drawing by Degas better than the colourful disasters daubed by artists of today? Colour is a snare and a delusion, so let me say my last word on this subject by pointing out that you don't have to see every detail to recognise the truth – or a nice juicy rat, as the case may be.

Although they want you to think they've covered everything in the account above, they don't even mention the most important function of the cat's eye – very understandable when you think that no cat of my acquaintance would reveal the secret, even under threat of torture. However, I will venture to tell you all the same, in the name of science: even if I do reveal it, the knack will still work. To put it in simple terms, the main function of our eyes is to make human beings comply with our needs and our own ideas, rendering them powerless before us. It starts when a human being still hasn't decided whether or not to adopt a cat. A hypnotic gaze from our eyes will do the trick, and the victim thus bewitched is immediately convinced that future life would be bleak and pointless without the music of that charming miaow. You could call it a kind of brain-washing, for I could give many other examples of ways in which we can bend humans to our will by means of a commanding glance. If the contents of the food bowl insult our sense of taste, we have only to exert a little icy eye contact to make our humans, as if by remote control, swap the meal just served for some delicious new flavour from a tin. And demanding delicacies from the dining table (often erroneously called 'begging') is another exercise performed with the aid of this quasi-telekinetic method. I could go on and on, enumerating our ways of indoctrinating humans with our eyes while they remain unaware of it. Human beings just cannot resist the glance of a cat – or so they think! And they don't know how right they are. Our two authors might stop to wonder why they're so keen to popularise an animal which is already popular in the first place. Because it has come to my ears that this couple of humans too are harbouring some of our secret agents, who whisper to them now and again, 'Here's looking at you!'

Keeping an Ear Open for Mice

The acoustic world of the cat

The cat's ears constitute an extremely sensitive and precise monitoring device which leaves human hearing far behind in almost every way. It is not surprising that an advertising campaign for a hi-fi stereo system in the top price bracket features the stylised ears of that small tiger-substitute the domestic cat. Cats need to have very good hearing because, as Desmond Morris explains, unlike dogs or human beings they cannot bring down their prey by means of lengthy pursuit. The cat is a typical sprinter without much stamina, not a marathon runner; it prefers to lie in wait for rats and mice and catch them by cunning. However, this means that its ears must register every tiny rustling sound. They must also be able to locate the precise position of the victim.

What we describe as sound is actually a wave of air

molecules rushing up, rising, and falling again; it is created every time an object moves, and spreads in all directions. However, between the vibration that has been set off and the hearing of the sound there is an ingenious set of obstacles to be negotiated, reminiscent of a miniature crazy golf-course with all kinds of cunning tricks such as winding and branching ways, circles, graduations and systems of levers. The molecules, once stimulated, roll towards the ear like tides and set the eardrum resonating. This resonance, in its turn, is transferred to three tiny bones picturesquely called the hammer, anvil and stirrup. These three little bones push fluid in the inner ear against membranes touching tiny hairs, which in their own turn press surrounding nerve cells, and the nerve cells carry the message to the brain. The whole process bridges the barrier between air and water: sound from the air is picked up, converted into liquid waves, and finally transformed into electrical signals.

The cat's aural range begins, like that of humans, at a lower limit of twenty vibrations per second (20 hertz) and runs parallel to human hearing up to about 500 hertz. From this point on, however, the cat easily outstrips us, and its hearing is even better than the dog's. This is because the human auditory nerve has 'only' 30,000 fibres, while the cat has some 40,000 'telephone lines' between ear and brain. Moreover, its ears are ideally situated directly next to the auditory centres of the brain, so that nerve impulses have only a short distance to travel. We can pick up acoustic vibrations up to a frequency of about 20,000 hertz, roughly the sound range of a violin. The sensitivity of the cat's ear, however, goes up to 50,000 hertz in the ultra-sound area, and perhaps even further. Even that does not qualify cats for the *Guinness Book of Records*: mice can hear up to about 95,000 hertz, and guinea pigs are the world champions with an upper limit of 150,000 hertz.

Although adult cats, according to the usual data quoted, register sound vibrations up to 50,000 hertz, three-week-old kittens hear twice as well – i.e., up to 100,000 hertz. While she is suckling her babies the mother cat also has particularly acute hearing, up to 80,000 hertz, precisely the wavelength on which the ultra-sound noises proceeding from the kittens' laryngeal area lie. They use these sounds to communicate with each other and to call their mother when she has left the nest. The kittens lose their super-auditory powers as soon as they leave their mother and siblings, and the mother's hearing becomes less keen when she stops suckling them. It is not especially unusual for females to develop a particularly acute sensory system when in an 'interesting condition'. It has been known for some time, for instance, that women in early pregnancy have especially keen senses of smell and taste. The hypersensitivity often expressed in morning sickness is presumably to protect the unborn child from tainted foods which might cause malformations.

Recently devices have gone on sale in American stores which look like miniature foghorns and are fixed to both sides of a car. When the car reaches a speed of about fifty-five kilometres an hour, the wind passing over the little horns produces a high, whistling sound which gives a warning to dogs, cats, game and other animals. The sound is much too high to be picked up by the human ear, but it sounds like an alarm siren to a cat going for a leisurely walk.

Not surprisingly, cats hear especially well in the frequency band containing the sounds naturally made by small prey animals. Where we hear radio silence, to the cat's ear the ether is full of chirping and whispering and the other mindless chattering noises mice make. In the upper octaves which humans can just perceive, the cat needs only one thousandth of the acoustic energy which we must expend to hear anything. And it is easy for cats to listen in to mice because they are extremely talkative little creatures, constantly whispering and chattering away in order to keep in touch with their fellow mice. These squeaks, which are outside the range of adult human hearing, are like vocal feelers. Small children can pick up some sounds in this frequency band; the rest of us will get an acoustic impression only if one of the mice happens to have a deep bass voice. It was said that the ancient Chinese bred mice with bass voices for their 'singing', and kept them in cages like canaries. The song of the house mouse is probably very romantic; at least, the song of its relation the harvest mouse is. These charming little rodents can be heard trilling tender love-songs in the mating season. Mice are not at all shy and have a distinct turn for music, which can be their downfall.

The squeaking sounds of mice and rats picked up by the human ear are in fact the lowest frequencies these rodents produce. They are close to the upper limit of our own auditory range, at 20,000 hertz. But even if our ears could pick up the higher sounds we could hear them only if we were very close indeed to the creatures making them. High frequencies do not travel great distances because they are quickly absorbed by the ground, by undergrowth, even by the air, more particularly in mist or fog. Consequently rodents can communicate with each other in their underground tunnels without announcing their activities to all and sundry. On the other hand very low frequencies, in the infra-sound area, travel long distances very well. Many whales use them for communication. The United States Navy uses this sound channel for the SOFAR ('sound fixing and ranging') system used to help keep submarines on course. The same physical phenomenon occurs, irritatingly, when we hear only the thudding rhythm of the music being played next door.

Obviously these small rodent chatterboxes have no notion that anyone is listening in to them, rather as tabloid reporters may listen in to the police radio. They would do well to take the wartime slogan of 'Careless talk costs lives' to heart. However, it is not the domestic cat but its medium-sized, spotted African cousin the serval who has the most acute ability of all to pick up rodent CB radio. The serval, with its huge, upright, fly-away ears, can even hear rodents chattering underground. It has also developed a crafty hunting method involving digging and waiting. When it picks up a suspicious sound, it looks for the entrance to the burrow and scratches a hole with its strong, curved claws. Then it sits in front of the building site it has excavated with paw raised – well aware that many rodents will make haste to repair any damage to their homes. At the first sign of movement, the deadly paw comes down, flinging the stunned prey aside, and immediately follows up this blow by delivering the *coup de grâce*.

This aural sensitivity to the sounds made by mice is the reason why even small kittens react with eager anticipation to certain appropriate sound signals, says Michael W. Fox.

Anything that rustles, crackles or in any other way suggests rodents will arouse great interest. Cellophane wrappings from packaging material make ideal kitten toys. On one occasion, the cat's keen hearing in the ultra-sound area is said even to have foiled the Russian secret services, according to the biologist Christoph Kühl. The Dutch ambassador in Moscow had two Siamese cats who discovered several microphones hidden in the wall. As these bugs worked on an ultra-sound basis, the cats thought they were mice, their hunting instincts were aroused, and they clawed frantically at the wallpaper to get at them.

Rat-catchers are frequently shown with pipes in old pictures, and not just after the remarkable events in the city of Hameln (spelt Hamelin in Browning's famous poem). This detail possibly indicates a method of dealing with vermin which did not involve poison, deriving from early ethological knowledge. It has long been known that animals react to synthetic sounds, and there must have been people in the past who lured rodents acoustically and then disposed of them. There are two pipes in Hameln Museum which were used by an Englishman called Heywood to lure rats out of their holes, a feat accomplished on a waste tip in 1953 in front of an assembled audience. Previously, the American farmer William Morell had discovered by chance that a rat's cry of pain and warning would keep other rats away. But not until 1983 did a Salzburg firm announce that it had developed an electronic device to deter rats and mice with high frequency sounds.

Like the cat's eyes, its ears are also of outsize dimensions by comparison with the equivalent human organs. If we were built on the scale of feline proportions, our ears would be twice the size they are. However, the funnel-shaped ears of the Felidae family are in fact even larger than they look from the outside because of their broad bases, which are hidden in the cat's fur. Furthermore, these feline radar screens are manoeuvred by thirty different muscles and are as supple and flexible as the body of an Indian yogi. They can be turned in a sweep of a hundred and eighty degrees and directed towards the source of a sound signal, like those huge dishes which radio astronomers use to try to detect extra-terrestrial signs of life. Our ears work with a mere six muscles, and we think it remarkable if a person can manage to waggle his ears very slightly. Of course the cat can position its mouse-locating system even more precisely by turning its head in the direction of the sound-waves. As the two natural directional microphones are on opposite sides of the cat's skull, all the acoustic vibrations are received by the sensors with a time lapse of milliseconds, and at different volume. This stereo effect is analogous to the optical overlapping of part of an image, and the brain converts it into an impression of direction. Together with the irregular, asymmetrical form of the ear muscles and their high mobility, it gives the cat the ability to locate the origin of any sound precisely. Cats can easily locate two sounds whose sources are at an angle of only five degrees apart. That is to say, from a distance of two metres, the cat can distinguish even sources of sound only eight centimetres apart. From a distance of twenty metres the cat still has no problem in checking sounds originating forty centimetres apart.

The difference in volume as received by the two ears,

however, can be transformed into a spatial stereo impression only with high-frequency sounds: in fact, only when the wavelength is shorter than the breadth of the head, and when the sound-delaying effect of the head itself comes into play. This means that sounds in the lower part of the audible spectrum provide no information to help in locating their source. Many modern hi-fi systems too have an additional third loudspeaker box, the sub-woofer. This component, which reproduces only deep bass sounds, can be placed anywhere you like in the room. Human beings (and cats) simply cannot say from what direction these very low sounds are coming. The dull rumbling of a heavy lorry sets everything around us vibrating, but we cannot locate the sound's place of origin. If mice would stop their castrato piping and communicate with each other in a deep bass, cats would be baffled.

Experiments of this nature have in fact been made – with owls, but their results could surely be applied to mammalian beasts of prey. Mice were allowed to run freely among dry leaves in a darkened room. The owls found and ate their rustling prey in thirteen out of seventeen experiments. However, if all the rustling noises (above 8,500 vibrations per second) were blanked out with a special sound filter, the owls never managed to catch the mice at all. And finally, if all sounds were blanked out in the range above 5,000 hertz, the owls did not even move from their perch. The sub-woofer mice must suddenly have seemed to be everywhere and nowhere. In fact it is lucky that most mammals are half deaf to the lowest frequencies, or they would always be picking up the vibrations of their own bodies. If you put your hands over your ears, for instance, you will hear a kind of soft sea surge which is produced by the rhythmic muscular contractions of the arms and fingers.

The size of the cat's ears helps us to draw conclusions about the geographical origin of different feline species. Because of their relatively large surface area, the ears can drain off heat and act as a kind of air conditioning in excessively hot weather. Large jumbo-size ears therefore suggest a tropical origin, while small ears suggest that a cat comes from an area with a moderate climate. Persian cats, with their comparatively tiny ears, probably originated in steppe country where there was not much sun.

Whether in miniature or outsize versions, however, the ears of the cat also act as a means of communication with its own species, complementing feline body language. Even in the wild, cats will abandon their solitary enclaves on occasion and make contact with other cats, whether to make approaches to the opposite sex, lay claim to territory, or simply to socialise, sometimes rather roughly, in a kind of club or fraternity. If social contact is to run smoothly, the cat needs appropriate body signals to show other cats how it is feeling. A slight forward tilt of the ears shows that the cat is in a calm and relaxed mood, 'all ears' for whatever may happen. If the cat goes on the defensive because something has upset it, the ears are laid back against the skull as if for protection from any injury. Just before the cat loses its temper the ears adopt a very strange attitude; they are suddenly tilted so far forward that if you are facing the cat you can see the backs of them. This dramatic signal indicates internal conflict: the cat

is torn between contradictory impulses, and may fly off the handle any minute.

The simplest form of learning is conditioning, and the first kind of conditioning to be discovered was in connection with a domestic animal's sense of hearing. The Russian physiologist Pavlov's dog always heard a bell ringing before it was fed; after a while its mouth began to water at the mere sound of the bell. The pairing of the unconditioned stimulus (eating) and the conditioned stimulus (the bell) produced a conditioned reflex. It is obvious that cats develop many conditioned reflexes in connection with the everyday sounds of their homes. Many cats associate their owner's imminent arrival with the sound of a car engine or with certain characteristic footsteps, and will be ready to put out the red carpet long before their human companion actually appears. The sound of the opening of a tin or the opening and closing of a fridge door can rouse cats apparently dead to the world to wakefulness.

But while Pavlov's dog allowed itself to be conditioned in a typically dog-like way, the relationship between the cat and its 'trainer' can be much more complex and interactive, or so at least it would appear from a remarkable chain of conditioning and counter-conditioning for the authenticity of which Roger Caras vouches. A friend of his put a small television set at the foot of her bed, a set that could be switched on and off simply by pressing a button. After a few days she was abruptly woken at five-thirty a.m. by the raucous noise of an early morning sports programme. She was alone with her cat, who was sitting by the television set looking bewildered. Since she was now awake, she got up and gave the cat his breakfast. This turned out to be a fatal mistake. The conditioned reflex remorselessly followed its course. Today Caras's friend has to make sure she has unplugged the TV set from the wall before she goes to sleep, because otherwise she is sure to get a Pavlovian reminder about breakfast in the small hours of the morning. When you stop to think about it, it is hard to be sure who conditioned whom.

A similar anecdote – a positive picture-book example of classic conditioning – is told of a monastery cat in medieval Germany. A tradition tells us that this intelligent animal always pulled the rope of the monastery bell when the cook was putting out the meat rations on a platter. The cook obeyed his conditioned reflex and turned piously to his prayers, while the cat obeyed its unconditioned reflex and tucked into the monastery menu. If the story is true, it was a cat who discovered the classic method of conditioning, long before Pavlov tried it out on his dog. Apparently the monks were so proud of their cat's powers of reasoning that they decided to give it an extra helping every day, and the bell-ringing with which it continued to pay homage to the power of educational theory over a grumbling stomach served as their dinner gong.

The background noise of human beings in conversation is probably a kind of 'white noise' to cats, all part of the acoustic background in general. It is even thought that certain fine hairs in the outer area of the cat's ear are constantly producing vibrations of their own. This would apparently produce a basic background of noise against which all sound-waves coming in from outside must assert themselves. If humans speak directly to cats, they almost instinctively

assume a high, Mickey Mouse type of voice. They usually emphasise long vowels such as 'ee' which are situated right on the feline wave-length. However, this seems to be a sign that we instinctively attribute infantile characteristics to the cat; when talking to dogs we do not employ the same acoustic strategy of 'talking down' to them so often.

The fact that we humans can speak at all is connected with the way we so easily choke: our larynxes lie very deep in our throats. The larynxes of cats and other mammals are situated much further up so that they can go on breathing even while they eat. In the course of evolution, language must have become so important that it was worth the risk of choking attacks. But even if other mammals had a larynx set low down, and a tongue placed so that it could produce the same sounds as talkative mankind, they still could not speak. To do that one needs a particularly sophisticated coordination centre called Broca's area, in the frontal lobe of the brain.

The cat who is snuggling comfortably against its owner's chest probably enjoys the relaxing, rhythmic heartbeat, something that gave it a sense of security even as a foetus before birth. Small orphaned kittens should have a clock with a loud tick put in the nest with them to imitate the maternal pulse. Human beings can blot out or filter out distracting sounds or sounds for which they have no use from the cacophony of acoustic environmental pollution. After a while someone living near a railway line perceives the sound of the passing trains only as a vague echo. With a little practice, you can hear the one conversation which interests you through all the shouting at a cocktail party. It seems reasonable to suppose that the elegant, relaxed and comfort-loving cat can also filter out certain sounds; otherwise, what with all the shrill, loud, rattling and grinding sounds of modern life, what with vacuum cleaners, washing machines, kitchen gadgets and other modern contrivances, they would surely go out of their little minds. In addition, all these mechanical contrivances must be generating various harmonic waves, secondary frequencies and parallel vibrations which human ears, with their limited reception range, do not pick up at all.

The other extreme, life in the eternal silence of deafness, is of course a tragic handicap for as sensual a creature as the cat. Fortunately, cats suffer from deafness less than other domestic pets. While up to thirty per cent of some breeds of dog are deaf from birth, the percentage of deaf cats is considerably lower. It is a well-known fact that white, blue-eyed cats are the most likely to have inherited this handicap, but even among white cats only one per cent have to grow up without the luxury of a sense of hearing, according to the veterinary surgeon George M. Strain.

Many cat owners do not realise their cat is deaf until it is over a year old. Before that age, the little bundle of fur's odd behaviour is more likely to be ascribed to wilfulness or plain stupidity. Deaf kittens are usually much rougher than normal kittens with their littermates, because they cannot hear their squeals of pain and thus go too far more often. On the other hand, they themselves mew and wail particularly loudly if removed from the home nest; as they cannot hear the rest of the family they are particularly dependent on direct physical contact.

Deaf cats are hard to wake up at mealtimes, and as a rule will respond only to a direct touch. The same is true of cats who are deaf in one ear and sleep on that side. They will often react aggressively and snap at the person who disturbs them. Humans who lose their hearing often develop paranoid characteristics too, and become obsessed with what people may be saying about them. If you observe deaf cats closely you can diagnose their condition from their failure to turn their ear muscles rapidly in the direction of a source of sound. Many vets are in favour of euthanasia for deaf kittens to keep them from a deprived life, one which in any case is often cut short by traffic or some other unpleasant accident. With loving care, however, such cats can be successfully reared. It has been shown, for instance, that they can be conditioned to respond to light signals in the best Pavlovian manner.

Many people and animals lose their hearing late in life after being treated with so-called ototoxic drugs – such as certain antibiotics – which attack the sound-sensitive cells in the cochlea of the inner ear. In humans this form of deafness first announces itself with an imaginary ringing sound in the ear described as tinnitus. We cannot, of course, listen in to the subjective world of cats who have just gone deaf, but the American anatomist John A. Pickrell suggests that they too are plagued by acoustic hallucinations of this kind. The poor creatures will react extremely violently to the smallest sound, will suddenly hiss for no reason, or snap angrily at imaginary enemies. The phantom sounds are probably heard because cells near the damaged area lose their natural inhibitions and fire off abnormal impulses which give the brain the illusion of sound. The degeneration has a sympathetic effect on the area regulating balance, which is also situated in the inner ear. Affected animals stagger about in an uncoordinated way in the first few days, and frequently vomit. Humans in the same situation often have violent headaches, but no one can say whether a newly deaf cat's decorative skull is throbbing too. After a while such symptoms die away again because the brain is compensating for the loss with optical information and the sense of touch.

It is probably just a myth that a love of music links cats to their two-legged companions, one of those legends that have been spread about the Felidae family since the days of ancient Egypt. The idea that cats like music probably developed because in the course of their lengthy sexual orgies, lust-crazed cats utter wild, loud cries which seem to be a terrible caricature of a concert and are known in English as caterwauling. The German word is *Katzenmusik*, cat music. Writers and artists, however, have always claimed to detect a liking for music in the feline nature. It is a subject raised in the enchanting *Philosophy of Life of Murr the Cat*, whose author, the great Romantic writer and musician E. T. A. Hoffmann*, immortalised the memory of his own pet cat in the novel.

The book recounts the life history of Murr the tom cat, narrated by himself, with delightful undertones of wit and

*Translator's note: Ernst Theodor Amadeus Hoffmann (1776–1822), best known in the English-speaking world for the story on which Tchaikovsky's *Nutcracker* ballet is based, wrote many other short stories and two novels, including *Murr the Cat*. He was not only a writer, but an artist, musician, composer, critic, and in daily life a lawyer. He features as the principal character in Offenbach's opera *The Tales of Hoffmann*. He died at the age of only forty-six. *Murr the Cat* has never been published in English, but a translation is at present in preparation, and will be issued by Penguin Classics.

irony. Murr grows up with his master, the stern Master Abraham, and develops a fine taste for music in his cultured home. He also has a shrewd eye for pretentiousness, whether in two-legged or four-legged creatures, and occasionally strikes up a song himself, for instance at another cat's funeral. 'It is a well-known fact that singers of our kind are perfectly able to express the deepest grief, the most desolate lamentation; they may sing out of longing or unrequited love, or in memory of a beloved lost one, so that even cold, unfeeling humans are touched by such songs, and can give vent to their sad feelings only by swearing strange oaths.'

Hoffmann put some surprisingly vivid and ethologically sound observations of the domestic cat into his book; for instance, Murr goes around at night with a rowdy band of male companions of his own kind, who show remarkable similarities with the student associations of the day, and are described as a feline fraternity. In many respects Hoffmann's description anticipates the studies of cat fraternities published by Leyhausen many decades later. This intuitive novel, which has inspired many later milestones of feline literature, will appeal to any cat-lover. Since Murr was so popular when the first two volumes were published around 1820, although the novel as a whole remained unfinished on Hoffmann's death, the writer Hermann Schiff produced a sequel in 1826 (*The Literary Remains of Murr the Cat*). Finally, the East German writer Christa Wolf, following in the footsteps of the great Hoffmann, wrote a story in 1970 called 'A Cat's New Philosophy of Life'. Its hero, the conceited tom cat Max, who expressly introduces himself as a descendant of the noble Murr, lives with a professor of psychology called Bartel, but can run rings round his master, whom he calls 'mine host', where knowledge of human nature is concerned.

The cat's relationship with music is actually much more prosaic than it is represented as being in the fine arts. It is a fact that all cats hate any kind of music when it rises above a certain volume. Even at normal volume their sense of hearing is aroused in a way that almost reaches the pain threshold; even Mozart played too loud will upset them. With wise foresight, many cats make themselves scarce as soon as their owner's finger touches the power button of the stereo system. Others are more easy-going and will 'respond' to one kind of music or another when its special sound emanates from the loudspeakers. That could be because in cat language certain notes convey a clear and instinctively fixed meaning, according to Desmond Morris. Crying kittens, for instance, mew at a certain pitch, and if the same sound occurs in a piece of music, female cats in particular may become very disturbed.

The excitement tom cats sometimes display in response to music can probably be explained by its similarity to a queen's imperious love-song. French zoologists conducting a survey in 1932 claim to have ascertained that cats are sexually stimulated by the note E in the fourth octave. If this is true, it would mean they have perfect pitch, a gift dying out in the human race. And if the cat shows alarm while hearing music, certain notes have probably reminded it of squeals of pain uttered by its own kind.

The 'cat organ' of medieval Brussels was constructed with occult ideas in mind, not to mention an atrociously sadistic mentality. Its sound came not from organ pipes but the heart-rending squeals of cats. Philip II was present at the first performance given by this 'musical instrument', in fact an instrument of torture for animals. Only an old drawing of it has been preserved. Instead of the usual pipes the instrument contained twenty cats in cages, each with a cord fastened to its tail. When a key was pressed on the organ, the corresponding tail was pulled and the cat uttered its cries of complaint. It is even said that the organ was played by a bear at its première. One cannot but wonder how Bruin was induced to get through the score. The point of the thing was presumably to conjure up sounds from the 'other side'. It was believed at the time that our earthly music was merely a poor imitation of the transcendental music of the spheres. As the cat was thought to be in league with the Devil himself, no doubt the devisers of the organ wanted to draw not heavenly sounds but at least a few bars of hellish music from its throat.

Quite early in history, people were already trying to borrow from the cat's acoustic repertory and reproduce it with musical instruments. The ancient Egyptians imitated the hissing of the cult object which had thrown in its lot with theirs on an instrument called the *seshesh*. A similar natural sound made a comeback with the sistrum of ancient Greece. The notes of the Japanese *shamisen* lute sound like the universal mew of feline vocal communication. In some circumstances this may be to do with the fact that the instrument is frequently covered with catskin. Catgut used to be the material generally used for the strings of string instruments. Today many expressions of sound in the animal kingdom, such as the song of the whales, are digitally recorded and incorporated into pop music. One can hardly help noticing how many musicals, symphonies and popular hits of recent years have associations with the way cats express themselves acoustically.

In any case, the most exciting sounds a cat ever hears very probably come from the vocal repertory of other cats. Michael W. Fox has worked out that the cat can produce exactly sixteen separate vocal patterns; Morris says that a blind musician claimed to be able to distinguish a hundred different sounds made by cats. Domestic cats have an acoustic vocabulary which is initially adjusted to communication between mother and child, and then changed and adapted for use in maturity. The ordinary 'miaow', the cat's characteristic everyday sound, is a rather unspecific announcement which may be used as a question, a request, or an expression of surprise or contentment. In the words of Hoffmann's Murr, the cat has 'the wonderful ability to express joy, pain, delight and wonder, fear and desperation, in short all the feelings and the passions in their every degree with that single little word "miaow". What is human language, compared to this simplest of all simple means of communication?'

However there is also a silent miaow. The silent miaow is a real acoustic gesture. The cat's mouth opens to mew, but no sound comes out. The writer Paul Gallico was so enchanted by this silent miaow that he wrote a whole book about it. He came to the rather down-to-earth conclusion that the cat's silent miaow is designed to hypnotise those humans who are privileged to look after it to do things they would otherwise not do (for instance, produce some desirable delicacy). Small kittens exploring the area just outside the nest for the first time, however, occasionally purse their mouths and make

tiny cheeping sounds in the ultra-sound register which human ears cannot hear, thus keeping the mother cat informed of their whereabouts. Perhaps these are early forms of the silent miaow.

Most cats have a small but expressive 'vocabulary' for conveying all important messages to their humans (out/in; please/thank you; help me; hungry; come on, do, get a move on!). Loud and lengthy sounds are mainly reserved for exchanging information with other cats and are uttered with the mouth wide open. The longest conversations are conducted in the course of the cat's sexual adventures. As a prelude to these sensual marathons the calling queen will utter an unmistakable cry of invitation which sends the young toms of the neighbourhood wild. At the climax of her flirtation the queen will frequently produce a guttural sound not unlike purring which signals her readiness to go 'all the way'. Finally, after the act of mating the ecstatic queen will utter the unique high scream which follows copulation.

Cats can growl or wail angrily, they can grumble, chatter, caterwaul and scream with pain. One of the most violent sounds they make is the furious hissing which they utter when confronting a hostile opponent. According to one very popular theory, the hissing cat is practising mimicry and imitating the terrifying hiss of a poisonous snake. Mimicry is the term for the tactics of dissimulation employed by certain creatures which take on the external features of other species, in order to profit by their advantages. For instance, many non-poisonous moths imitate the striking warning colours which adorn the wings of other, poisonous species, thus giving themselves the protective appearance of being poisonous too. Desmond Morris, who seems to have been the originator of the theory that feline hissing is mimicry, may perhaps have let his imagination and taste for poetic analogy run away with him here. Any adversary who could really mistake a hissing cat for a snake must surely be blind, feeble-minded or suffering severely from hallucinations. Cats hiss at each other too, and can hardly be expecting one of their own kind to mistake their identity. Moreover, lions, tigers, pumas and leopards use the same acoustic threat. Why should these heavyweights of the cat world need to use the hissing-snake bluff? The idea of being confined in a telephone kiosk with a tiger is just as alarming as the notion of encountering a rattlesnake, as Roger Caras points out.

The most flattering, pleasing and seductive sound a cat (or indeed any other living creature) can make is purring. The sense of comfortable pleasure conveyed by this long-drawn-out sound, reminiscent of a rolled 'r', instinctively transfers itself to the human observer. Purring indicates genuine approval, and is the ultimate you could wish for in the way of Zen Buddhist relaxation. If purring did not exist to indicate animal well-being, it would have to be invented. People who could purr would be bound to make friends. When a cat being stroked and petted reacts with silence it is like a snub: we feel that something is wrong. An old German word for the cat's purr was *spinnen*, 'spin', referring to the gentle and regular hum of the spinning wheel. The *Oxford English Dictionary* defines purring as 'a low continuous vibratory sound expressive of contentment or pleasure'. Technically, purring is a pulsating sound of about 25 hertz, and suggests a desire for contact to continue.

It seems that besides the domestic cat, only jaguars, pumas, ocelots, servals, cheetahs and the red lynx can purr; Charles Darwin regarded lions, jaguars and leopards as acoustically handicapped in that respect. It is not quite certain, however, whether this applies to the king of beasts. At the end of the last century African railway workers shot some lions who, according to the accounts which have come down to us, uttered a 'terrible purring'. Some domestic cats are not particularly good at purring, while others indulge in the comforting sound with endless enthusiasm. The temporal dimensions are remarkable. Cats can purr for hours on end without any change of rhythm or intensity. Tiny kittens purr with their mouths closed shortly after birth, keeping the sound up even while they breathe in and out. This is something of a puzzle, for in the animal kingdom most sounds are produced when the air current makes the vocal cords vibrate as the creature breathes out. Kittens briefly interrupt their gentle purr only when swallowing. Their purring is probably a significant signal to the mother, stimulating the milk flow. The mother herself purrs: a feedback from which the kittens can gather that all is well. Older kittens sometimes purr at their mothers with great enthusiasm, perhaps with a view to getting an extra helping of milk.

In an adult cat, the infantile signal is converted into an expression of pleasure and willingness to be friends. The purr is useful here because cats, unlike dogs, have few signals in their body language conveying an attitude of goodwill towards others, says Michael W. Fox. Dogs can lick you, raise a paw, rub noses, and have other forms of fraternising too in their repertory; that solitary hunter the cat, on the other hand, is limited to a restricted code. However, there is one drawback to the theory that purring is a signal of pleasure and comfort, and many students of cat behaviour have come up against it. Cats purr not only when they are obviously feeling pleasure, but also when they are in pain: while kittening, when injured, at the vet's or even (as with the lions mentioned above) on the point of death. In a book on European wildcats, the zoologist Rudolf Piechocki of Halle University in Germany tells us that these wild forest creatures, whom it is usually impossible to approach, utter a deep purring sound when caught in a trap.

Trying to make sense of these anomalies in a roundabout way, some writers have fallen back on an argumentative conjuring trick. It is the same as the trick used by Sigmund Freud, the father of psychoanalysis, to defend his theory of dreams against its critics. According to Freud, our nocturnal visions all serve to satisfy suppressed unconscious wishes. In that case, replied his sceptical contemporaries, we ought never to have nightmares or dreams which arouse anxiety. Very well, said Freud, many of these secret wishes are indeed of a depraved and perverted character; the dreamer's anxiety and sense of discomfort merely show that he is horrified by his baser instincts. These days the inappropriate purring of the cat in certain unpleasant situations is sometimes interpreted in a similar way. The cat who purrs at the vet's is begging for mercy, so to speak; it reverts to infancy and acts the part of an innocent, vulnerable kitten asking to be treated gently.

This will fit the notion that the purr is indeed a sound of pleasure, but has sometimes become slightly twisted. But the explanation may be much simpler. Perhaps the inappropriate purring has more in common with an attack of hysterics. After all, human beings themselves sometimes give vent to unseemly hysterical laughter on hearing a piece of dreadful news. A cat who produces a purr while in pain may simply be trying to decrease stress. We ourselves, in the dentist's chair or in similar situations of discomfort, have a tendency to counter anxiety with pleasant fantasies. In fact it is known that in mammals painful and distressing stimuli cause the production of endorphins, the body's own painkillers. The mammalian brain is trying to mitigate states of extreme agitation, whether of a positive or negative nature, and to replace them by conditions which tend the other way. In this case we might say, by way of a simplified explanation, that purring is the cat's opium.

In spite of the pleasing effect of the purr, scientists have had a great deal of difficulty until very recently in understanding its mechanism. Over a long period heated arguments were conducted about the way in which the cat produces this ecstatic sound. One explanation was that during purring the false vocal cords vibrate; these consist of two folds of skin situated behind the real vocal cords. There was also an ingenious theory that purring is the result of turbulence in the bloodstream of the main vein conveying used blood from the body back to the heart. Somehow or other the cat's positive mood was supposed to create turbulence in the blood and produce violent vibrations which, in a complicated anatomical process, would make the skull resonate.

Quite recently, however, a group of researchers headed by the biologist Dawn Sissom of Tulane University in the USA, working in collaboration with the zoologist Gustav Peters of Bonn, succeeded in gaining real insight into the workings of the feline sound mechanism. In an unusual bugging operation, the researchers fitted ten cats with several extremely sensitive microphones, some of them applied directly to the coats of the feline guinea-pigs. The sound patterns they obtained were divided into pitch areas and made visible as a spectrum on an oscilloscope. The measurements showed that the purring sound consists of a regularly recurring series of very short pairs of pulses which the human ear cannot hear separately. The volume is about sixty-five decibels, the equivalent of quiet conversation. The acoustic profile of purring does not depend on the cat's physical build or its age. The individual quality of a cat's purr is probably inborn and will remain the same throughout its life. But in any case, the experiments showed that the actual purring sound is produced by uninterrupted vibrations of the larynx. If you touch the throat of a purring cat you can actually feel the vibrations. Cats are artists in sound, and can easily make other sounds while they are purring; a common miaow can be superimposed on the pleasant purr.

In the final analysis, the sound is caused by the way the muscles of the larynx rhythmically open and close the glottis – the gap between the two vocal cords – causing the air stream to quiver as it passes through. The rhythm is created by the activity of an 'impulse generator' in the brain, not by the resonance of the breath. If the right nerve centre is stimulated purring is bound to ensue. That means that this basic feline sound is more of a gentle tremor engendered by the nervous system than a vocal expression. Or you could compare it to a buzzer taking its buzzing signal from electrical switch-gear. Incidentally, the human laryngeal muscles have a beat of up to 30 hertz; if we had the cat's rhythm generator in our brains we could probably purr too. As things are, the best we can do is to place the tongue against the roof of the mouth as we breathe out in order to produce a poor imitation of a purr.

Tigers, who cannot purr because of the difference in the structure of a tiger's larynx, produce a pleasant noise of contentment of their own, resembling a quick, jerky f-f-f-f sound. They use this sound, rather like the snorting of a horse, to express a conciliatory frame of mind when they meet other tigers. Their friendly gesture can be spotted some distance away, because as they produce the sound these majestic creatures swing their heads vigorously up and down. A tiger trainer who hopes to survive his job has to master the f-f-f-f sound, says the American tiger behaviourist Bill Fleming. If a tiger does not answer a human's acoustic attempts to approach it with the same pleasing sound then something is very wrong, and the human can confidently look forward to his next incarnation. Like the purring of the domestic cat, says Fleming, the ecstatic tone of its big relation is very appealing to humans. The tiger likes to rub its head against the body of its opposite number throughout the greeting ceremony, showing every sign of pleasure. Even real tigers can be cuddly.

Comments by Francis

At first glance there doesn't seem to be anything wrong with this chapter, but take a closer look and you'll spot enough lies and half-truths to make your fur stand on end. The worst mistake they've made, in fact you could almost call it an insult, is saying we don't understand music. Now no one would claim that my colleagues and I are enthusiastic Guns 'n' Roses fans, but I can assure you there's no other species on earth better able to appreciate the Goldberg Variations than the various members of the Felidae family. Personally, I sometimes prefer a nice bit of orchestral composition. Wagner and Co. provide perfect background music for my daydreams of cats taking over the world. Here I owe much to my human companion Gustav, who has so far resisted any temptation to turn in his Stone Age record player and get the CD kind instead. Better sound on CD, you say? Easier to use? Well, not for me, because once the owner of the aforesaid record player has gone to bed, I can indulge in my own supreme musical pleasures. Once I've set the turntable rotating I put out the sharpest claw in my paw and place it carefully in the groove. A bystander would hardly hear a thing as the acoustic vibrations are transferred up my front leg to my body, which immediately becomes an excellent resonator, and finally to my head. I am thus totally immersed in the music – no need to go the long way round involving the ears – and become a part of it myself. There's not much risk of damaging the vinyl discs, unless I happen to nod off. If we ever do get a CD player I'm thinking of simply short-circuiting myself to it.

Oh yes, and another thing: the authors think my kind hear the chatter of the humans who serve us as nothing but 'white noise'. If only that were true! Day after day, our ears are contaminated by the most appalling of humanoid excesses: marital quarrels, gossip, telephone arias, whispered sweet nothings that don't mean a thing, and other pernicious nonsense, no end of it. I am firmly convinced that the constant brainless chatter of humans is to be equated with the slimy trail snails leave behind them – they just can't help it. We, on the other hand, confine ourselves, as the authors have correctly

recognised, to the most essential communications, since there is no need to waste many words on even the most important things in life. A penetrating miaow is quite enough to let an uninvited guest know that you intend to empty your bowl unaided. And another miaow, this time with a languishing tone to it, informs the lady of your heart that the moment has come to see about ensuring the survival of the feline race. It's as simple as that. So all you lords of creation out there, do us a favour from time to time: keep your big mouths shut.

CHAPTER 4

The Smell of the Great Wide World

The nose: the gateway to the cat's soul

People of a suspicious cast of mind will say that 'something stinks' and they can 'smell it a mile off'; they 'scent trouble', 'smell a rat', and it 'reeks' of something undesirable. Kindlier souls follow their noses in the other direction and believe that life comes up 'smelling of roses'. Such figures of speech show that the sense of smell is inseparably intertwined with emotional judgements and instinctive attitudes, even though our own olfactory sense is nowhere near as good as that of the high-powered noses of our domestic pets, who can pick up scents even in a tiny homoeopathic dilution. Human beings, having neglected the sense of smell in favour of the intellect, can identify just sixteen aromas by name if they are offered several hundred familiar scents in an experiment. But even our restricted sense of smell has one thing in common with the sensitive noses of the Felidae: its main function may be described as hedonistic, in that it almost always arouses feelings of attraction or dislike. Pleasant scents tempt us to come closer, while an unpleasant smell is defined by its repellent character. The smell of decay and rotting arouses intense dislike, and the smell of vomit can often set off an unfortunate chain reaction.

In spite of these rudimentary features we have in common with the cat, its olfactory performance is so immensely superior to our own that we may confidently regard it as a kind of sixth sense: nasal clairvoyance, so to speak. Although the cat has only a small head with tiny nostrils, the surface of the interior nasal cavity is artificially increased by means of several shell-shaped indentations. The breath that is drawn in makes its way through a positive maze of bones and folds, adding up to a surface area of forty square centimetres covered with olfactory mucous membrane. The human nasal cavity does not have even half this amount of surface area for scent absorption. Cats catch the gaseous molecules in the air stream with sixty to seventy million microscopically tiny olfactory cells and turn them into nerve impulses, while human beings have only five to twenty million – at the very most – of these olfactory receptors. In all cases, receptor density is the criterion of sensitivity. For instance, our fingertips are very sensitive because they are covered with a close mesh of tactile receptors, while the comparatively insensitive upper arm has a much smaller receptor density.

Tiny hairs or cilia protrude from the olfactory cells in the olfactory area. They catch the scent molecules and move to and fro in the air current like sea anemones on a coral reef. Cells of this kind occur only in the nose, and are renewed on average every thirty days. In this they are distinct from all other nerve cells and receptor cells in the body, which are not restored once they have given up the ghost. The olfactory area is moist and yellow, and contains fatty substances. The intensity of the yellow coloration is a criterion of the sensitivity of the nose. The stronger the colour, the finer the sense of smell. Albinos have a very poor sense of smell and thus a pale olfactory area. The olfactory area of the cat is an intense brownish mustard colour, while the human equivalent is light yellow. It has also been shown that dark-skinned people have a darker olfactory area, and thus, in theory, ought to be able to smell better.

Even the cat, however, does not have the best natural sense of smell in the world; the German shepherd dog has an olfactory mucous membrane covering some one hundred and seventy square centimetres and containing two hundred million olfactory cells. For some strange reason the tiger, though an excellent hunter, seems to have a very poor sense of smell; as David Taylor says, this raises many questions. But most animals with good noses go on all fours with their heads close to the ground, where the moist, heavy scent molecules are concentrated. This is true of both the cat and the elephant, which usually lets its trunk hang right down.

Of all living creatures, man is the only one who opens his mouth when sneezing. Cats, like dogs and horses, keep their mouths closed and sneeze inwards through the nose, holding their breath for a moment. It has been calculated that the air expressed in sneezing reaches eighty-five per cent of the speed of sound, which is certainly fast enough to expel bacteria and other foreign bodies. The American writer Diane Ackerman tells us that scientists regard this as the purpose of the sneeze.

The cat's olfactory universe is so different from ours that imagination can give us only a vague idea of it. The cat moving from one corner of the room to another may well have experiences during that short trip as intense as those of a human being moving between olfactory extremes: imagine first, perhaps, a strong scent of vanilla assailing the nose as it wafts out of an ice cream parlour, then the unpleasant stench of a neglected public toilet, next moment the ethereal fragrance of violets. The cat's nose reacts with particular sensitivity to smells containing nitrogen compounds. This enables it to reject food which is tainted or going rancid and therefore gives off nitrogenous chemicals. Cats are much more fastidious than dogs in their reaction to rotting food; they like everything to be as fresh as possible, never 'ripe' or stale. The cat cautiously circling a bowl of something hot is probably suspicious of the smell rather than the heat. However, lions are an exception; they will even eat stinking carrion dripping with ptomaine. At the other extreme is the cheetah, which gorges itself only once, and that briefly, on the blood and liver of its freshly killed prey, and shuns meat that is at all gamy.

Cats in frequent contact with each other probably recognise their acquaintances much better by smell than by sight. In favourable circumstances the greeting ceremony begins with mutual rubbing of cheeks and noses, after which a cat will courteously raise its tail to expose its rear end for inspection and anal checking by the other cat. It is thought that both parties learn a lot about each other's identity, health, sexual condition and so on during this ritual. In the process, moreover, the cats' individual scents, produced by their glands, mingle into a bouquet.

Human beings in many cultures would also rather rub noses than shake hands as a greeting. This is the custom among the Eskimo, the Maori and the Polynesians. Such a greeting lasts rather longer than a hand-shake, and is often accompanied by satisfied grunting. Other peoples put their heads together in greeting and breathe in their visitors' aroma. Many scientists believe that one reason we like kissing is a strong desire to smell the face of the beloved, where his or her individual scent is particularly intense. Among many peoples, for instance in Burma, India and West Africa, the word for 'kissing' is the same as the word for 'smelling'. Finally, the members of a tribe in New Guinea say goodbye by touching each other's armpits, then rubbing their hands over their own bodies, and thus taking on the other person's aroma.

Cats who live in colonies of some size even produce a collective or tribal smell by superimposing their scent markings, and this smell also acts as a boundary to keep outsiders away. The British biologist David Macdonald gives an account of a colony of feral farm cats leading an unusually social life. Some of the kittens being reared by the colony were killed by a hostile intruding tom. Directly after this violent deed, the shattered colony began an agitated process of mutual anal checking. This was probably the only direct (and reassuring) way of being certain that the murderer was no longer among them. In small newborn kittens, the nose is the first sensory organ able to function. When the kittens have moved a little too far from their mother they can find the way back to the source of security by their noses. Each of these little bundles of fur is also imprinted on a particular teat by its smell. This makes a lot of sense for members of a hunting species. Hungry little mouths can make straight for the source of milk without any argument when the over-worked mother cat lies down to nurse them, and the busy huntress herself can set off again quickly when stores are running low.

It looks as if hopes of finding an effective deterrent scent to keep the persistent cat away from certain places or objects must be banished as an illusion. There are indeed various anti-cat sprays on the market, but they are the kind of thing which people tend to try once, put away, and never use again: the manufacturer is appealing exclusively to first-time buyers. When a cat keeps urinating in the wrong place or constantly scratching a valuable piece of furniture, it would certainly be nice to have a chemical deterrent which would work like garlic on vampires or holy water on the Evil One. The Dutch ethologist Matthijs Schilder once conducted a consumer test of all seven cat repellents on the market. These substances consisted of 'essential oils' and/or 'ketones' along with 'natural scent substances and sulphur compounds'. He was trying to find out whether these substances would keep cats from eating and drinking, or urinating and defecating. The results were not encouraging: none of the substances had any measurable deterrent effect, and indeed one of them, containing nothing but essential oils, actually had the effect of attracting the small feline hooligans. Compare Desmond

Morris's account of various natural anti-cat substances, in one of his best-selling cat books. According to Morris, as long ago as the days of ancient Rome the leaves of rue, a small shrub with a strong smell, were used to keep cats off. However, contact with rue leaves can bring some people out in a rash. Onion juice, which lingers much longer in sensitive animal nostrils than in the duller human nose, is said to have proved very effective. But some cats will actually regard this natural tear-stimulant as a culinary enrichment of their diet. Finally, Morris suggests that ordinary household vinegar may have a strong deterrent effect because the acid aroma irritates their sensitive nasal passages. Scepticism is to be advised, since Morris himself concludes that cats are tenacious animals and may well regard such chemical warfare as a challenge.

Unlike human beings, but like some other animal species including horses and rattlesnakes, cats have a third chemical sense somewhere between smell and taste. The vomeronasal or Jacobson's organ, which is responsible for it, is a tiny sensory device located in an indentation in the roof of the mouth, and is activated by scent molecules. Cats sometimes make a strange, rather foolish-looking face, lips curled and nose rumpled. It is known as the 'flehmen' reaction; the animals are 'licking' olfactory substances out of the air and conveying them by means of the tongue to the sensory organ in the roof of the mouth. 'Flehming' is most easily observed in a snake analysing the flavour molecules brought in on its forked tongue. In a sexual context, only tom cats display the flehmen reaction when they pick up the intoxicating and seductive emanations of a calling queen; female cats, however, will 'flehm' when they are investigating an area marked with a stranger's urine. The Jacobson's organ is not connected with the scent centre in the brain which analyses messages conveyed by the nose and gives them emotional content. Instead, the nerve impulses produced when a cat is 'flehming' go straight to the hypothalamus, a kind of processing centre deep within the diencephalon or interbrain. This walnut-sized structure contains among other things the brain's 'red light districts', connected with the sexual drive, and has a great influence on hormone production. It also contains the cerebral 'pleasure centre', which will switch the organism into a state of euphoria if it is electrically stimulated. The function of the vomeronasal organ is rather mysterious, but Fox suspects that the cat's sexual drive and territorial behaviour would be much restricted without it. However, similar symptoms occur if a viral inflammation destroys the air passages of the mucous membrane, as Bradshaw points out. The cat loses its appetite, develops 'dirty' habits, and ignores willing sexual partners. But then again, we can never be sure whether both chemical senses were not impaired by the same infection, which has causes similar to those of our common cold. The nerve centre which processes impulses from the Jacobson's organ seems to produce irresistible behavioural impulses in the cat, particularly where the opposite sex is concerned. Just how the Jacobson's organ interacts with the sense of smell is still a mystery. Roger Caras suggests that there may be a parallel with a stereo system, where the sound is regulated by two separate but related settings, bass and treble.

Cats keep in almost constant touch with other members of their own species, communicating by means of marking. It is a method of communication which humans can imagine only dimly, and consists of leaving scent marks produced by the glands behind at certain strategic points. This chemical bottle-post – a kind of open letter to whom it may concern – is sending messages of a hormonal nature in the shape of substances called pheromones which produce such unequivocal reactions in their recipients as sexual interest, territorial aggression, and so forth. The advantage of the relatively long-lasting medium employed is that the message will still come across even in the absence of its sender. Like a memo, it can contain information about who, when and where the sender was, while he himself enjoys the protection of anonymity, since his present position cannot be precisely located. This is why a cat making scent marks may also leave a little package of something solid behind. Marking is particularly useful when it is difficult to convey visual or acoustic signals, for instance at night or in thick vegetation.

Pheromones, meaning literally 'convey excitement', are also contained in the drops of urine which dogs like to leave on trees and water hydrants. The message is intended for all other dogs and conveys an unmistakable claim to ownership. Deer make use of at least six different pheromones in marking the boundaries of their territory, impregnating the air with their libido. The most effective pheromone known in nature is produced by moths; even from a distance of miles, the male moth will home in on a tiny drop of the female's scent. In mammals, however, the reaction to pheromones is not such an automatic reflex as in insects, and consequently these substances are sometimes described as 'social perfumes'. With their complex brains, mammals have a higher degree of freedom in their behaviour and make use of a wider spectrum of stimuli and configurations in planning their conduct. But monkeys and apes have pheromones, and male chimpanzees whose noses are stopped up will not be seduced by even the most explicit advances from a lovesick female. It has even been claimed that in *Homo sapiens* the vagina contains certain attractive substances called copulins, although this tale sounds about as reliable as the story of the Loch Ness Monster.

The question of whether humans actually do communicate through pheromones is one of the more mysterious areas of human biology. A little while ago scientists claimed to have found a sexually alluring substance called androstenon in underarm sweat. Androstenon, with a smell somewhere between urine and musk, plays an interesting part in the love life of the pig. Even that animal's keen nose for truffles is to do with the fact that the buried fungus gives off this piggy scent. Initially, it appeared that men found pictures of women more attractive if they smelled of that 'certain something', and in preliminary tests women could perceive more sex appeal in men giving off the aroma. Today, however, excitement about the alleged pheromone has died down. To half of all experimental subjects the hormone-related substance smells of urine, and try as they may they cannot find it attractive. But while various firms are still selling deodorants by the ton to ensure that we retain not a whiff of our natural odours, another branch of the cosmetics industry is busy trying to patent human pheromones such as androstenon. Pheromone sprays called Boar Mate are obtainable in the stock-rearing trade, and pig breeders use them to make the sow more receptive.

It is also a fact that after a while women living in close proximity have synchronised menstrual cycles. Even if all they do is get a daily whiff of another woman's armpit sweat, their menstruation will soon adjust. A famous experiment testing the sense of smell in the two sexes has shown that women can smell the musk-like substance exalotid at a concentration a hundred times lower than is required for men to pick it up. Women's keen noses function best around the time of ovulation, when they are much more likely to comment on the 'high' smell of game if they are eating it. Finally, the case of people suffering from anosmia, loss of the sense of smell, shows how deeply we are still rooted in the olfactory world. These unfortunates sometimes have so little appetite that they develop anorexia, and may lose all interest in sex. Cats who have lost their sense of smell because of some defect also frequently suffer from loss of appetite, leading in extreme cases to anorexia, as described by the American physiologist Kimberly May. However, the cat's appetite is not always impaired by anosmia, so that the connection between its nose and other physical pleasures would seem to be rather more complicated.

Cats are lavishly endowed with glands allowing them to register information about inanimate objects, living creatures and places. Among the places where these glands are located are the forehead and lips and around the anus. We have all seen a cat rubbing its head on a wall in a state of delight, or pressing close to walls or other objects as if in a trance. A hundred and fifty years ago, Giovanni Raiberti came to the poetic but erroneous conclusion that the cat intended this behaviour to express its sense of being romantically at one

with the world and the universe, 'reminding us of those Arcadian shepherds who, in their lovesickness, would talk to trees or the moon or try to soften stones'. Reality can seem rather prosaic by comparison.

The most notorious anal glands of all belong to the skunk. The glands at the rear ends of carnivores like the cat are contained in anal sacs, which can be two or three centimetres long in the case of the lion. These appendages work like a chemical laboratory, turning the original homogeneous secretion into a pot-pourri of subtle scents. You can sometimes see secretions coming from the anal glands of domestic cats when they are excited. In conditions of great stress, cats will sometimes secrete the entire contents of their rather small sacs.

In the normal way, the human nose cannot pick up the messages left by the cat's glandular activity. However, there is an exception: the secretions from the anal glands of the female give off an unmistakable aroma at certain times of the cat's sexual cycle. Roger Tabor describes it as 'cheesy'. When the cat rubs its head against certain items in order to mark them, it will instantly fall into a trance-like state of bliss. The eyes are closed with pleasure, and the softest tones of ecstasy of which a living creature is capable rise from deep within the throat. The greatest hypnotic effect is produced by places already given the olfactory stamp of approval by other cats. Sometimes the recipient of the scent message begins to salivate, pushing off from the ground with the hind legs so that the lips can take in yet more of the smell of the great wide world. The animal sometimes becomes so ecstatic that its body is shaken by little jerks and twitches. As a crowning touch to this euphoric ritual, the tail glands usually add their own signature to the open letter. You can observe the whole sequence closely when a cat presses close to its owner in ritual greeting; first it rubs round the legs, then pushes its whole body against them, and finally winds the full length of its tail round the olfactory monogram thus created.

It seems to be very important to the cat for all friendly members of its 'family' to exchange physical odours in this way. The idea is to enable individual aromas to mingle in the collective group scent mentioned above, which gives the animal the comfortable feeling of being at home. However, David Macdonald observed that some of his feral cats preferred to be on the receiving end of the rubbing, while others preferred to be actually doing it. It seems that the high-ranking cats at the top of the social ladder receive more affectionate rubbing than the subordinate cats. As a rule the human protector of a multi-cat household will receive the largest share of these proofs of goodwill, since he or she rules as wielder of the tin-opener. Areas and localities also get marked, and many cats mark the outer limits of their territory by smearing the secretions from the pads of their feet over the ground like paint.

Spraying urine is the most obvious way in which cats mark out their frontiers. In this particular form of urination only a little actual urine is produced. The cat's quivering tail is held erect, and fine drops of spray are aimed at the target area. A confident tom will turn round and spray a few drops of his strong-smelling natural product at the borders of his territory, and will then sometimes move his rear end and tail over the liquid, to make sure his marking is well distributed. As

Macdonald discovered in his experiments, toms generally sniff and 'flehm' at messages left by strangers longer than queens do, whatever the sex of the cat who left them. Secretions left by cats from outside generally arouse more interest than the home-made variety.

Leyhausen has compared these scent-markings with traffic lights, regulating the traffic and reducing the number of encounters to the necessary minimum. A fresh spray of urine (red light) means the place is out of bounds because someone else is enjoying its amenities. A stale marking (green light) shows that the coast is clear because no one has staked a claim to visiting rights recently. However, if scent-markings are traffic lights, then cats frequently commit road offences. Latecomers often fail to be impressed and leave fresh scent markings. They may add their signature in more solid form too, and then go on their way undeterred.

In the feline world, love's arrows come tipped with unambiguous scent messages. The procedure starts when a tom cat goes courting and tracks down his willing love object by her scent markings. These chemical love letters also contain extensive information about the queen's state of oestrus. Tom cats regularly seek out new locations, and will travel a considerable distance when they have smelt a promising message from the seventh heaven of delight. It is well known that several suitors will 'read' the scent message put out by a female advertising for a partner, so they usually have to compete with a number of rivals in a tournament of love.

The loud cries of a courting tom, the shrill screams of the noble knights engaged in combat, and the equally shrill calls of approval from the object of their affections once she has chosen a mate have made the cat a notorious sex symbol. To a considerable extent, however, the criteria whereby a queen chooses her mate are still unknown. All we are sure of is that among cats, as among the overwhelming majority of all mammals, the female makes her own selection. According to the principle of female choice established by Charles Darwin, the female decides which male may combine his genes with her own.

Females tend to play coy, and will take great care to accept only those sexual partners who have certain important and desirable characteristics and fulfil their requirements. Males, on the other hand, employ rather lax criteria in choosing their female partners. The reason for this is the difference in parental investment. In most species, females invest much more time and trouble and more resources in the business of reproduction, while males make a far smaller contribution. Members of the sex investing more in the next generation have more to lose in mating with 'inferior' partners. Members of the sex investing less have more to lose if they do *not* mate. In other words: females have to be choosier because they have more to lose if they make a mistake, whereas a mistake made by a male will cost him only a weary grin.

The queen on call is especially fastidious when she is choosing her lover from the group of suitors. During battle, however, she usually sits somewhere near, apparently unconcerned. Scientists who have studied cats conclude that she is not obliged to grant her favours to the winner of the tournament, as one might expect, since dominant and victorious toms could probably contribute 'superior' genes.

The queen will sometimes ignore both victor and vanquished and give herself to a third party not involved in the fight – indeed, she will often do so while the others are still locked in combat. Sometimes a queen remains faithful to one tom cat over several periods of oestrus, taking no notice at all of the battles of her other suitors.

The precise circumstances are at present being investigated by several groups of researchers, but it is suspected that female cats 'follow their noses' in choosing a lover, and will accept him only if the chemistry is right. We know much more about this principle in mice, whose fate is of course fatally linked with that of our domestic tiger on the hearth – literally linked, by way of the food chain. Female mice go strictly by smell in choosing a partner, and do not think male mice sexy unless they have a body smell which clearly diverges from the female's own. This divergence tells her that the male has a very different heredity. She needs to know this to avoid inbreeding, which could lead to the emergence of latent (recessive) hereditary defects. In mammals, individual body smell is determined by recognition signs called antigens which are situated in certain cells of the immune system. This essence, whose pattern derives from hereditary information, is as individual and unmistakable as a fingerprint, and manifests itself in the odours emanating from the body.

The latest research has shown that mice can even tell the state of health and general genetic fitness of a male from his smell. In experiments, male mice were infected with a single-celled parasite which affects the intestinal tract. The researchers then observed the way female mice responded to the males' urine and other strong-smelling traces they left.

Result: a 'good match' sprayed his charms liberally around, while a sub-standard mouse was conspicuous for the small trickle of his emissions. Consequently, the females thought the healthy males smelled good, while the waste products of the infected animals aroused panic and aversion. The parasite obviously ruined the sex appeal of the males, although at this point they were not yet displaying any recognisable symptoms of illness. The females also wrinkled their noses in disgust when they smelt males carrying a particular gene called the T-allele. This is an abnormal hereditary factor which leads to sterility and high mortality in offspring. Altogether, it would be a strange thing if the cat too, with its great sensitivity to smells, was not influenced by the obsessions of its nose in matters of love.

However, even if the calling queen gives herself relatively indiscriminately to the waiting crowd in the heat of passion, it is still extremely probable that the chaff will be carefully separated from the wheat, at least in her genital tract. Among those animal species which enjoy orgies of promiscuous sex during the fertile period, the struggle to hit the bull's-eye is partly carried on within the female's reproductive system. The female cat usually mates with several lovers during oestrus, and their sperm will compete for the privilege of fertilising her. This eventful scenario means that there will often be a mongrel mixture of kittens in a single litter, each with a different father.

However, genetic egotism impels every tom cat to produce as much sperm as possible, giving him a maximum chance of passing on his genes. After all, every organism in nature tries to produce as many viable copies of its heredity as it can.

Eckart Voland, a sociobiologist at Göttingen, says that the more males have access to the female at the same time, the greater is the rivalry between their sperm, and the heavier are their testicles in relation to general body weight. Cats are world champions of the animal kingdom here: their ratio of testicles to body weight is one to a hundred and eighty-one, while in dogs it is one to seven hundred and twenty-seven and in monogamous (or relatively monogamous) man it is one to one thousand seven hundred and eighty-five. Naturally it is worth while for individual tom cats to outdo their rivals in the sheer amount of ejaculate they produce, sending as many sperm as possible into the race. This makes sense, if only because the vagina, as protection against any germs that may enter, presents a very hostile, acid environment which kills many sperm cells.

However, this arrangement is mainly advantageous from the female's point of view too. If for some reason the female is unable to assess the quality of her mate from his outward appearance, her best strategy is to instigate active competition between sperm. In the Olympics held in the microcosm of the female's body, the best man ought, after all, to win. It is even thought that the female's egg can recognise the quality of the sperm it encounters from certain chemical signals, and will actively give precedence to the best of them. However, there may be constant competition in the female cat's genital tract – between the male principle with genes aiming to survive at any price, and the female principle wanting the right to choose. It is even thought that tom cats (and human males) may produce special 'kamikaze' sperm whose sole purpose is to eliminate competing gametes. If this theory is correct, then only one per cent of sperm are intended to make it to the egg; the rest are killer sperm lying in wait for their rivals at strategic points and disposing of them by some unknown means.

Up to a certain point, says Voland, competition between sperm has developed in humans too. There is some evidence to support this idea. Men separated from their sexual partners for some days were found to ejaculate particularly large quantities of sperm. Perhaps they were taking the possibility of infidelity on the lady's part into account. In that case, the enemy's sperm would be suppressed by superior forces. Human sperm remains viable in the female genital tract for up to five days; it has recently been found that women prefer to risk an adventure on the side at times when they are still carrying viable sperm from their regular partners. Perhaps this timing plays the 'old' and 'new' gametes off against each other.

The cat's habit of covering up its faeces by shovelling earth over them with its paws is almost always regarded as a sign of its extreme cleanliness. The line of argument is that cats are very hygiene-conscious and dislike the smell of excrement in their living quarters. It is certainly a very deep-rooted instinct, for cats who have no earth, sand or cat litter available will drag along all kinds of objects from the vicinity to cover up the offending substance. According to Morris, however, this behaviour is more characteristic of a subordinate cat who fears annoying the higher-ranking cats with the smell of its excretions. Dominant cats will actually deposit their royal excrement in prominent places, so that the common herd can show a proper respect for it. A domestic cat, Morris says, always seems to have clean habits because it accepts its human owner as supreme if uncrowned chief.

However, it appears that independent of the cat's social standing, faeces are always buried when they are produced at the centre of the home range. Strict rules of hygiene are relaxed only on the periphery of the feline estate; it is here that the faeces are on public view. In fact communal cat latrines can sometimes be found in these peripheral areas, particularly if the space available for individual lavatories is restricted, but only the local members of feline high society may use them. Faeces left at these public latrines are usually neatly buried, although unattractive little offerings are some-times found there, left stinking to high heaven and uncovered in a manner not considered typical of cats. Then again, however, one can never be sure whether a 'dirty' cat has been performing, or whether scratching over the spot has simply exhumed a previous burial.

An explanation for the cat's meticulous hygiene which seldom attracts much attention is that cats do not want to scare off their natural prey unnecessarily, in particular rats and mice. Pliny the Elder, that prolific Roman writer, was already perspicaciously suggesting this in the first century of our own era: 'They scrape earth over their dirt to cover it, so as not to betray their presence to mice.' Numerous experiments have in fact shown that rats and mice react with terror and alarm when they pick up the scent of their enemies' faeces. Similarly, ungulates lose all interest in food when they smell the faeces of lions, leopards, tigers and lynxes, as the American veterinarian Paul J. Weldon points out. In some places the faeces of big cats are scattered on purpose to keep deer and other ungulates away from certain areas.

However, it is most improbable that the deer who were the subject of such studies in England could still have a buried memory of the smell of lion and puma dung at the back of their minds, since such a memory would have to go right back to the Pleistocene epoch. It is more likely that many animals who are eaten by other animals pick up the characteristic smell of carnivore dung in general. It may be that the remains of meat in the dung, decomposed by secretions and intestinal bacteria, give off particular scents which instinctively warn the prey animals of a terrible fate awaiting them. Perhaps human beings who eat a lot of meat have only to let wind to scare mice and rats away.

In nature, however, the roles of hunter and hunted are not always strictly defined, and they can change from one moment to the next. Even tigers sometimes have to beware of beasts of prey intending to kill them. For this reason, the domestic cat too can obviously tell from the scent trails of certain enemies that the coast is not clear, and there is deadly danger waiting somewhere nearby. The Texan biologists Jeannie Wright and Paul J. Weldon came to this conclusion when they got fifteen cats to smell the glandular excretions of the pytas snake. The pytas is a non-venomous monster over three metres long, which will greedily swallow all kinds of vertebrates. The cats in this experiment were all 'naïve' animals: that is to say, they had been brought up indoors and had no experience of the perils of the great outdoors. In spite of this lack of experience, they instinctively showed dislike, and made it clear that they were not at all happy with what

was going on. Cats sometimes react in a similar way when they encounter the vomit or excrement of unfamiliar animal species, say the scientists. The experimental cats also immediately lost their appetite for delicious cat-food tainted with the offensive scent traces of the pytas. Another reaction seems absurd at first glance: the cats rubbed their cheeks against the markings and frequently passed their paws over them. Similar behaviour had already been observed in American ground squirrel. It is thought that the animals instinctively try to cover up their own smell with the enemy's by way of camouflage. This would in fact be a very effective tactical move, since snakes orientate themselves almost exclusively by chemical stimuli when hunting. It seems that over the thousand years of their evolution, cats have got it well into their heads that they must beware of snakes.

One of the less attractive aspects of keeping cats is the fact that they produce surprisingly large quantities of excrement for animals of their dimensions. This is because, as pure carnivores, they can allow themselves the luxury of a relatively short intestine. Their natural diet, unlike that of an omnivore, is notable for its ease of digestion. A meat diet needs to pass through the body quickly so that no putrefactive bacteria develop. Vegetable food, on the other hand, has to ferment for a long time so that the intestinal flora can decompose the indigestible greenstuff. Furthermore, the Felidae family with their short, intensive hunting techniques need very high acceleration values, so their intestines naturally weigh very little and will contain very little deadweight to hinder them. As a sprinter who performs best at high speed, the cat also has a racing pulse – the fastest of all domestic animals. Its heart beats a hundred and fifty times a minute, whereas the human heart beats just seventy times a minute.

The dog family, on the other hand, has specialised in a long, extended type of hunting which calls for larger stores of energy. Consequently, the cat's metabolism has a much lower degree of efficiency than the dog's. Cats extract only seventy-nine per cent of the energy from their food, while dogs extract eighty-nine per cent. In other words: more unused calories come out at the other end of the cat. As a result, its faeces are more liquid and less well formed than the dog's. As the British biologist Andrew Kitchener says, this form of energy loss can have surprising consequences: vultures do justice to the nourishing leavings of wild-cats, while they studiously ignore the excrement of the dog family, which has all the goodness leached out of it.

However, there is yet another and very unattractive living creature which has found its ecological niche in the results of the cat's intestinal activity: the single-celled parasite *Toxoplasma gondi*, which causes toxoplasmosis. According to the present state of knowledge, only the members of the Felidae family are the host for this parasite, which inflicts apathy, appetite loss and neurological disturbances on its four-legged host. Cats sometimes get this unpleasant parasite from eating a lot of raw meat or from eating mice. The excrement of the infected animal will then be contaminated with the micro-organism for a period of one or two weeks. According to statistics, just under one per cent of West European cats are infected with toxoplasma; the percentage is considerably higher in underdeveloped countries. Pregnant women should take care to avoid all contact with feline faeces; while

the parasite does no great harm to adults, it can harm unborn babies or even cause stillbirths.

Our desire to dispose of the end product of the cat's digestion and deodorise the olfactory evidence of it costs us several million tons of cat litter a year. It was once worked out that in the USA alone, enough cat litter is produced every year to fill the Empire State Building from basement to roof terrace two and a half times. Most manufacturers use fuller's earth as the main ingredient, a fine-grained clay which is very absorbent because of its porous structure. *Homo sapiens* has been making use of fuller's earth for the last seven thousand years, longer than it has used any other minerals except flint. About fifty years ago, a small entrepreneur in America discovered by chance that the fuller's earth he had used as a nesting material for chickens made an excellent lavatory for cats.

All kinds of other materials have been tried over the last few decades: wheatflakes, sawdust, ground maize, processed newsprint, even pounded orange peel. But fuller's earth is still the standard kind. Today, of course, everything is made into a business and a science, so the basic material is meticulously provided with many of the beneficial achievements of the chemical industry: fragrant essences, disinfectants, deodorants, ingredients to combat germs, fungi and parasites. Men in white coats systematically explore the most intimate products of the cat, all in the interests of the litter industry, subjecting the latest top-secret materials to double-blind testing for their hygienic and olfactory qualities.

The length of the human intestine, in relation to its size, is somewhere between that of a herbivore (like the cow) and the cat. By this criterion we are omnivores, just like the pig. Humans, like cats, have an instinctive dislike of the smell of their 'lower' body functions. Even perspiring armpits and other intimate sweat-producing areas do not meet with much erotic approval, and are usually deodorised. Although we seem to think little of pheromones, however, we are using more and more of the synthetic products of the cosmetic industry as an inoffensive substitute – sometimes paying quite indecent prices for them. We employ essential oils, perfumes, room sprays, deodorants and other forcible methods of subduing our olfactory environment to our obsessions. Car dealers have been known to spray an old banger with the smell of a new luxury model, with a view to making customers literally pay through the nose. Aromatherapists claim to eliminate character defects and neuroses with various natural essences, although not all the essences may be quite what they claim. Cats, however, take very little notice of our olfactory manipulations of our homes and our own bodies. They will honour us with their physical affection whether we have just showered and perfumed ourselves with heavy essential oils, or whether some unfortunate chain of circumstances means we have gone a couple of weeks without a bath. We do not seem to stimulate the Jacobson's organ at all, although cats have been known to show an obsessive passion for the underarm sweat of a person they know well. In other words, to the cat's nose humans are boring creatures; our personal smells are just not on the right wave-length.

There may be an exception in the shape of those unfortunate people who suffer from the rare disorder of fish-odour syndrome. This is an inherited metabolic defect which causes the person affected to give off a penetrating smell of fish from all pores in the skin. It is caused by an inability to break down the 'fishy' biomolecule trimethylamine, one of the amine family which occurs in many proteins in the diet, and is usually very soon made inoffensive. Those who suffer from this disorder may be physically healthy, but are usually the butt of mockery, insults and humiliation from an early age. It is hard to imagine a cat taking such an insult to its olfactory nerves in its stride; in extreme cases it might turn paranoid and become obsessed with the idea that someone was always keeping a nice fat herring away from it. On the other hand, the American anthropologist Louis S. B. Leakey believes that back in the mists of time our distant ancestors had a much stronger body odour, and one that we would greatly dislike today. Even the big cats, it is to be supposed, would have found it so repellent as to keep their distance.

If Leakey's theory is correct, it could explain why the cat did not come to live with humans until the time of the ancient Egyptians. Theirs is known as the first culture in history to have improved upon the natural human scent with perfumes and essential oils. They dabbed scent on their bodies to keep strange magic at bay, for medicinal and hygienic reasons, and to make their skin soft and supple. Potentates even built entire palaces of sweet-smelling cedar wood. In ancient Rome this passion inherited from the Egyptians went to such lengths that people would bathe in perfume – and sprinkle cats and dogs with it. At least that seemed to suit the cats better than the acrid body odour of Neanderthal man.

Cats live primarily on meat, with a bit of fish now and then, so they themselves are bound to have strong-smelling breath quite frequently. If you cannot stand the smell of animal tissue being digested, you would do better to keep a vegetarian pet, maybe a horse or a hamster. Mouthwash is not suitable for cats. There is no indication that bad breath makes cats lonely or causes difficulties in their love-lives. However, the normal smell of a cat's breath should be distinguished from the smell when it is sick. The former may be rather unpleasant, the latter turns the stomach. Really bad halitosis can indicate tooth decay or internal disorders, and is a case for the vet.

When a human brings some new object home – a box, for instance – it and the human's hands are subjected to a thorough nasal inspection on the cat's part, while the suspicious aroma of a strange cat can have as drastic an effect as a wife's detection of strange lipstick on her husband's cheek. Human means of transport are very confusing to the cat's olfactory methods of communication. Cats love to leave scent markings on car hub-caps and tyres, but when the marker comes back to check his certificate of ownership at a later date it may have mysteriously dissolved into thin air, or perhaps it has been completely replaced by a hostile monogram.

No really intelligent living being can spend its entire existence in a state of unrelieved reality: it needs some kind of release. All creatures with highly developed brains some-times use intoxicating substances as a way of breaking away from the grey everyday world. Desmond Morris suggests that cats are 'born junkies'. Given the right plant drugs, many cats will greedily drink in the smell until they are in a state of euphoric intoxication suggestive of an LSD trip with sexual overtones. We tend to think instinctively of drugs and hallucinatory substances only in association with humans – in fact with particularly evil or sick humans. The need for a 'high', however, is much commoner in nature than law-abiding citizens may think, according to the American psychiatrist Ronald K. Siegel in his book *Intoxication*. Among other examples, Siegel describes the case of African elephants who gorge on fermenting (and therefore alcoholic) fruits and will then trample through the landscape in a tipsy condition, making as much racket as hooligans after a lost football match. There are also birds who enjoy hemp-seed, containing hashish, and then flutter drunkenly towards the sky.

And then, of course, there is the cat, who loves to get high on the smell of catmint, valerian, and a few other plants that affect it in the same way. Catmint or catnip, *Nepeta cataria*, a member of the Labiatae plant family, is found in large parts of Europe and America. Its effective constituent is nepeta oil, which to the human nose slightly resembles both mint and fresh meadow grass. Certain insects smell the same, and are extremely interesting to cats; the insects use their scent, just like catmint, as a deterrent to other small and harmful forms of life. If you put a drop of nepeta oil on the body of a weevil being dragged away by ants, the ants will drop their burden instantly. They begin cleaning themselves frantically, and even ants who only touch their 'dirty' companions with their feelers will feel disgusted and clean themselves as soon as possible.

Cats can smell this etheric drug even in a dilution of one to a billion. The essence has the same effect on the entire Felidae family, from the lion to the domestic tiger on the hearth. The trip lasts five to fifteen minutes, and begins with intensive sniffing and 'flehming'. Then the cat begins to lick and munch the plant in a state of obvious ecstasy, purring, rubbing its whole body on the plant and the ground, rolling and occasionally even leaping in the air. In some ways this behaviour has much in common with the cat's natural sexual reactions, something that always becomes more obvious when a higher dose is given, according to Siegel. The flow of saliva increases dramatically, a tom will have an erection, while a queen utters her typical sexual yowl. On the other hand, some phenomena suggest something more like delirium and hallucination. For instance, many cats 'under the influence' will stare into space glassy-eyed, while others pounce on imaginary moths.

Many scientists, Siegel says, have suggested that catmint is a natural, seasonal aphrodisiac which gets the cat 'into the mood' to make love in the spring. However, only about seventy per cent of all cats are susceptible to the intoxicating smell; the susceptibility comes through a dominant gene.

If rats have nepeta oil sprinkled on them, it cancels out all a cat's hunting instincts. Indeed, the cat can be induced to abandon all dignity in the presence of its arch-enemy, adopting the motto, 'Make love, not war!' A really clever rat would carry a catmint leaf with it at all times, a preventative as useful as a wreath of garlic in Transylvania. Nepeta oil can now be bought as a spray, and is said to be used by lion tamers as an emergency brake if their charges become unruly. Unfortunately, trappers too have been quick to exploit this weakness of the Felidae family. Veterinarians sometimes use this mild plant medicine as a tranquilliser. Only a small dose is required to provide the cat with an ecstatic treat now and then; the effect is lost if too much is given.

According to the American biologists Arthur and Sharon Tucker we still do not know whether catmint is a real psychedelic drug with a hallucinogenic effect like LSD. The problem is that no active substance at all reaches the organism and gets into the brain. The intoxication comes solely from the contact of scent molecules with the olfactory mucous membrane. This is a unique phenomenon in the world of drugs consumption, since even people who sniff solvents to get a fix are absorbing actual chemicals into their system. On the other hand, a catmint trip is a considerably wilder business than a cat's normal state of sexual arousal. Nepeta oil is probably what is called a supra-normal stimulus, affecting the same receptors as the specifically feline phero-mones. Because of its unusual structure, however, the drug has an exaggerated effect which does not coincide with the original sexual programming. Humans too are affected by supra-normal stimuli: for instance, pictures of beautiful women manipulated to exaggerate key stimuli beyond their natural extent.

Apart from this, there are accounts of people smoking catmint in a pipe, and apparently having a very pleasing, contented and indeed intoxicating experience. Some of the hippies of the sixties thought catmint when smoked was a mild hallucinogen and not inferior to hashish. In many countries, the plant is even used therapeutically to treat spastic disorders. An English book of recipes from 1629 claims that extracts of catmint can bring on a woman's 'courses'. A recent reference book agrees that catmint is useful in cases of delayed menstruation. Given a wide interpretation that could mean that catmint may be used as an abortifacient, and such a drug may have been used to procure abortions in the past, which would be quite a sensational revelation of cultural history, providing the controversial morning-after pill with a long ancestry.

Siegel says that the Japanese herb *matatabi* or 'pleasure plant', which is related to catmint, has an even stronger effect on the Felidae family than nepeta itself. Big cats with access to this sinister substance were found to neglect all their natural pleasures for it – eating, drinking and even mating included. This was a genuine case of severe addiction, for the animals could not wean themselves off the 'hard drug' even when it began destroying their olfactory centres and brains (as in human addiction to solvent abuse). The most bizarre and adventurous case of feline drug consumption, however, is described by the Tukano Indians of the tropical rain forest. According to their accounts, jaguars can frequently be seen in the forest vigorously attacking the bark of the *yaye* tree. The Tukanos themselves partake of the same botanical delicacy before hunting, believing it will endow them with the jaguar's wonderful hunting skill and amazing eye. In fact the *yaye* does contain a hallucinogenic drug which enlarges the pupils and gives a 'high'. It also increases sharp vision and heightens perception of sensory stimuli. Perhaps there have been occasions when the jaguar itself, like the two-legged inhabitants of its own environment, has seemed to see a hunter doped with *yaye* sprout wings.

Despite their weakness for catmint, cats are strictly on the wagon. Unlike mice, who can easily be persuaded of the benefits of a dram, cats will be put off by the slightest taint of alcohol in their food, although there are exceptions in the shape of cats suffering from stress so that the balance of their minds is disturbed. This was discovered by early educational theoreticians at the beginning of this century when they induced what they called an 'experimental neurosis' in their laboratory animals. In these experiments, cats had to make what in itself is a simple distinction between clear geometrical shapes, for instance squares and circles. But then the tiresome scientists made the squares look more and more like circles, until the overstrained animals flew off the handle. In this extremely unfeline condition, they finally learnt to value the soothing effect of alcohol in eliminating stress. However, when the experiment was over and the animals pulled themselves together, they immediately gave up drink of their own accord. In normal circumstances cats are obviously too cool and collected to feel any benefit in intoxication.

Comments by Francis

Well, the world of smells is a tortuous one, and as our two clever friends correctly realise, no species knows more about it than mine. Human beings need a complicated array of instruments like faxes, computers and coils of tangled cables for indirect communication, but all we require is a straightforward, environmentally friendly spray on the side of a flowerpot to convey complex messages to whom it may concern. Our sniffing rituals are clear as day, passed on by nose to nose generation after generation. But these days it's getting more and more difficult for us to identify humans from their smells and find out what they're really like. Because although their noses, like the rest of their sensory organs, are ludicrously inferior to our own, they employ the good old method of deception here as elsewhere. It's this sort of deception, getting craftier every day, that now makes it virtually impossible for us to guess what they're really at. For instance, whereas you could once have identified Liz Smith from Accounts in Room 23, Corridor E, miles away and against the wind by her strong smell of cold cream soap modified only by a faint whiff of eau-de-cologne, these days the office junior may well announce her presence with the aroma of Chanel No. 5 or something even more expensive. This makes it really difficult to know who you're dealing with. Take the sixty-four thousand dollar question: is this shabby character emanating a strong and unpleasant male odour, with a three days' beard and wearing a sweaty undershirt, that mythical proletarian Stanley Kowalski from A Streetcar Named Desire, *or is he a top manager on the staff of IBM uncritically ready to copy any idiotic notion gleaned from* Vogue for Men? *Who can say for sure? I could go on for ever giving you examples of this aromatic Tower of Babel, because no one smells right for his station in life these days. The impoverished student uses the same aftershave as the Parisian man about town, and so far as perfume's concerned you can hardly tell the supermarket checkout girl from the decayed gentlewoman. There's been an aromatic revolution in the world of humans, and it has done considerable harm to our own authority in olfactory matters. Think again, or rather sniff again, is the motto of the feline race these days. But how do we even do that, when thriving industries are busy day and night enveloping their willing victims in increasingly impenetrable clouds of fragrance which only the chosen few could once afford? One way or another,*

humans just don't smell human any more. So I recommend our two hopeful hacks to refrain from making funny remarks about what may at first glance appear our bizarre methods of communication by smell. We aren't trying to manipulate others by olfactory means; it's your own kind who have probably lost any idea of what they really smell like by now. And when we Felidae pick up a sudden explosive whiff from the lower parts of a thoroughly scented person, a whiff immediately covered up by a sweetish perfume, it's pure nostalgia. Because then we know we're meeting a real human being!

A
Gourmet
on
Velvet Paws

*The cat's sense of taste and
nutritional drive*

Such figurative expressions as saying that a thing is 'much to one's taste', or that one has 'acquired a taste' for something, have a double meaning in many cultures. Those with 'taste' are people who have tried life out in their own way, and found parts of it wonderful but others wholly unpalatable. In the cat, an instinctive drive to find nourishment coinciding with the delicate palate of a French restaurant critic add up to an explosive mixture. If there is anything like original sin in the mysterious prehistory of our small feline friends, then no doubt it was the forbidden mouse of knowledge they nibbled in the Garden of Eden. In retribution, divine justice may well have reduced the palatability of rodent flesh, so that ever afterwards the fallen cat

would feel an indefinable urge to get its teeth into something better.

And setting out from that supposition, it is easy to see a mental link with the riddle of its self-domestication on the banks of the Nile (not to mention the phenomenal success of the pet-food industry). For there can be no doubt that the ancient Egyptians themselves must have fed their household animals various little delicacies on the sly, mice or no mice. The nutritional drive, after all, is the Achilles' heel of the cat, the weak point in its character which opens up the way to corruption, inconstancy and betrayal.

Hoffmann's hero Murr finds that out when, after a long separation, his previously unknown mother crosses his path. This lady, a single parent, is now indigent, living on the feline poverty line. In a passage full of sympathy, Murr decides to present her with a left-over herring head which, however, goes missing in his own jaws in transit 'in mysterious circumstances'. Initially tormented by guilt feelings, the perpetrator of the herring theft puts his rhetorical skills to justifying the deed on the grounds of lack of responsibility for his own actions, arguing that he had been in a state 'which, while it alienated me from my self in a curious manner, yet seemed to be my self indeed'. A tinge of remorse may be detected at first: 'Why did fate not make our breasts proof against the wild play of calamitous passions? O Appetite, thy name is cat!'

But soon Murr is retreating behind cynical rationalisation; he tells us he now realises 'that it is a crime to resist Mother Nature. Let everyone find his own herring heads, and not seek to be wise for others who, guided by a proper appetite, will soon find their own.' Murr also reacts with hypocritical indignation on discovering several degenerate young members of his own species down in the cellar, making themselves comfortable beside the mousetraps there and waiting placidly for whatever may transpire. 'As a cat of truly noble mind, I became quite heated, for I could not but note how the automatic action of those lifeless machines induced great apathy in the young toms.' The hypocritical if indignant moralist composes a pamphlet fulminating on 'Mousetraps: Their Influence on the Character and Initiative of the Cat', admitting, however, that his labours in writing it have left him no opportunity to put the heroism he himself demands to the test.

The main function of the sense of taste is to analyse the chemical composition of the food molecules dissolving in the mouth. This laboratory report goes back to the consciousness as a subjective taste experience. If there is something the matter with the results of the analysis, it creates an unpleasant taste sensation engendering dislike or even a desire to vomit. A favourable verdict, however, stimulates the appetite and implies that the contents of the mouth are right for the body's requirements. In the long term these requirements may take the visible shape of rolls of fat. The human sense of taste ultimately derives from four basic qualities: sweet, sour, bitter and salty. However, the relevant sensors are not designed to distinguish between abstract categories; instead, they give us the ability to identify groups of foods which our metabolism needs.

The taste cells – the nutritional instinct's 'identification squad' – are arranged in zones on the surface of the tongue. In

other words, the tongue is a kingdom divided up into provinces according to sensory talent. The front of the tongue is extremely sensitive to sweet and salty flavours, the side to sour flavours, and the area at the back is reserved for bitter flavours. The location of the taste buds for bitter flavours at the back of the tongue makes biological sense, because situated there they can make us choke if there is any danger of poisoning by bitter toxins. However, this arrangement should not be envisaged as one of rigid divisions: there are all types of taste buds in all regions of the tongue, and only their density differs.

Taste cells are linked to the taste buds in groups of about fifty units. The taste buds also form groups and combine to make up small swellings called papillae. Seen through the microscope, the tens of thousands of taste buds inside the mouth look like Martian volcanoes, and they gape on the surface like bats clinging to a damp, slippery limestone wall. The cow, of all creatures, although it does not have the reputation of a gourmet, has a tongue particularly thickly covered with taste cells; perhaps they are needed to extract something like flavour from its tough diet of grass.

The sense of taste is constantly working with the other sensory channels, in particular the sense of smell, and the end result is to give the palate a composite total impression which is difficult to separate into its components. Taste and smell share a common air shaft, like the inhabitants of a tower block who soon know when the neighbours are having lasagne for supper. What we experience subjectively as flavour is in fact usually determined by the smell of food. If a heavy cold puts your nose out of action, the most delicious of dishes all taste the same.

We also perceive smells much faster than flavours. With a cherry tart, for instance, you need twenty-five thousand times more molecules to taste it than 'just' to smell it. Every child knows that even cod-liver oil loses its terrors if you hold your breath while swallowing it. Moreover, most natural products evoke mixed impressions. For instance, a grapefruit stimulates those areas of the tongue which taste sour, sweet and bitter flavours. The fruit's essential oils, concentrated mainly in the rind, reach the nose and add the crowning detail to the grapefruit experience as a whole. But we all know that the eyes are involved too, and every true gastronome pays attention to the visual effect, which has a subtle effect on the palate. The mere sight of a meal arouses countless flavour memories, associations and conditioned reflexes which influence appetite one way or another. People taking part in a flavour test found that food dyed a strong artificial colour with harmless, neutral-tasting colourings – for instance, purple bananas – suddenly tasted unpleasant and indeed revolting. However, it is probably just a modern myth that you can deceive the cat's fastidious palate by putting a cheap own-brand supermarket cat-food into a tin which once contained the most expensive market leader. Even the placebo effect has its limits.

Finally, the subjective impression of taste also depends to a considerable extent on a channel of perception which lies somewhere between the sense of touch and the experience of pain. This is the trigeminal nervous system, which has sensors all over the face and head area, in the mouth and the nose. Basically, the trigeminal system is an alarm signal providing the brain with information about sensations of touch, pressure, and pain. Most of the more violent experiences felt in the head – from the effect of smelling an onion to a headache – are set off by the trigeminal warning system, and most chemical signals of a stabbing, burning, pricking, penetrating, biting or caustic nature are really perceived by the trigeminal nerves rather than the senses of smell or taste. The system is primarily designed to preserve the organism from the corrosive effect of damaging stimuli, such as harmful gases, but living creatures can become accustomed to trigeminal stimuli and even get to like them. A taste for onions, horseradish, fizzy drinks, mustard or dishes containing chili seems to depend largely on their trigeminal appeal. The reason for this culinary masochism is probably that violent stimulation of the trigeminal nerves sets off the endorphins mentioned above, which make us feel a curious 'painful pleasure' in consuming such things.

The trigeminal system provides the cat's only means of locating the spatial origin of a certain smell without moving its head. We should think of location of the source of a smell functioning in much the same way as spatial hearing; the differences between the two nostrils are converted by the brain into a kind of three-dimensional impression. Experiments have shown that the organism cannot determine where a scent is coming from if it appeals exclusively to the olfactory channel (for instance, the smell of vanilla), unless the head is moved. The reason is not entirely clear. The sense of smell obviously does not have a high degree of spatial resolution; smells are diffused around an area, so to speak.

Perhaps one reason is that in most living creatures, the nostrils lie too close together.

However, some species of fish are an exception: they are easily able to tell the direction from which a certain smell is coming. This is particularly true of the big sharks, whose nostrils, significantly, are set far apart. Moreover, these underwater killers sway their heads rhythmically from side to side, like a cat, reinforcing the three-dimensional visual impression. This process makes the spatial 'scent image' even more precise. Sharks, consequently, are always the first to surface near fishing boats when remains of fish are thrown into the water.

The cat can also locate a smell easily if the stimulus (e.g. the carbon dioxide in fizzy drinks) affects the trigeminal system. Mice must therefore give off a penetrating smell – as one can easily believe they do – if the cat can sniff out their hiding places without moving. But this is rather an academic observation. In realistic ecological circumstances, of course, the cat can simply swing its nose around and locate the mouse smell from its gradient – the differences of concentration in the air. We all instinctively do the same if we notice that someone near us has broken wind.

Taste is one of the least studied of the cat's senses, and many popular cat books keep perpetuating the same half-truths, myths and inaccuracies, which is rather surprising when you stop to think of the billions made by the pet-food industry. The cat's tongue, at any rate, has true taste cells at the tip, the root and the sides, while the papillae in the central area have small barbs pointing backwards, and are not concerned with the chemical analysis of food. They give the surface of the tongue the structure of a rasp and are used for grooming fur, lapping up liquids, and stripping the flesh of prey animals from their bones. In a tiger, Bill Fleming tells us, this rasp is so strong that it can take the paint off the wall of a house, and it makes very quick work of removing the bones of a gazelle from the valuable meat over them. Fleming has even seen a tiger lick frenziedly at a piece of wood which promptly shrank. However, as tigers have their tongues under better control than TV chat-show participants, their cubs are never in any danger of being licked to death in affectionate moments.

The accounts given in cat books of the kinds of flavour a cat's tongue can taste are notoriously contradictory. Almost everyone agrees that the cat can distinguish the basic flavours from sour to bitter and salty, with decreasing sensitivity. Some authors add that the cat can taste water better than any other living creature, an ability which humans almost entirely lack. Finally, many experts allow the cat an ability, either more or less marked, to taste sweet flavours. With one exception, their works say nothing about the scientific sources on which their statements are based; you get the impression that they have frequently copied from each other uncritically. The most persuasive account, however, is given by the British biologist John Bradshaw in his very thorough new work, *The Behaviour of the Domestic Cat*, which scrupulously cites original publications in academic journals. If his findings are to be believed, the cat lives in a world of taste which is very different indeed from our own.

In the cat, according to Bradshaw's account, the commonest type of taste cells, particularly dense at the tip of the tongue, are adjusted to respond to amino acids. These are the basic natural building blocks from which protein and thus meat foods in general are made. The taste buds react to many amino acids with increased excitement but to others with a decrease in activity. Cats like those amino acids which, like lysine, stimulate the receptor, while they ignore the varieties which will have an inhibiting effect. In this context, the term amino 'acids' does not denote a sour flavour; the human tongue tastes the stimulating amino acids as decidedly sweet, while the amino acids which the cat rejects are very bitter in flavour. However, that does not allow us to conclude conversely that 'good' protein-building materials taste sweet to the cat as well as to us. None of the cat's relevant taste cells react to sugar or sweet substances. We must simply suppose that there are wide spectra on the cat's taste horizons which our own palates cannot perceive.

The nutritional sensors described, which determine the cat's sense of taste, are very probably adjusted to separating 'good' and 'bad' proteins. This is a difficult process for us to imagine because our own palates have little sense of the composition of proteins. However, we should remember that an adult cat needs to derive at least twelve per cent of its daily energy from protein; an adult dog, on the other hand, can manage on a mere four per cent. The enzymes which break down protein so that it can be converted into valuable energy are extremely active in the cat and cannot be switched off. Consequently the animal can use much 'worse' proteins for the construction of body tissue than other living creatures. Presumably this is why evolution has developed the cat's sense of taste in a different direction from our own.

This fact could also explain certain disconcerting and persistent aspects of cat behaviour which have provided much material for speculation in scientific circles. Folk wisdom tells us that mice are top choice on the menu of cats, at least of cats living wild. Cats also like to hunt shrews, and do so very successfully, but they will not eat them. The unwanted trophies brought home by the cat as a present for its human owners frequently consist of shrews. There are several explanations: among others, that the glands of the shrew secrete an aroma which turns the cat's sensitive stomach. We suggest another hypothesis: the shrew contains 'bad' amino acids, and there is a good reason why. Unlike other mice, the shrew is insectivorous, and has a diet with a very high protein content (unattractive as those proteins may seem). Moreover, that fact is often its undoing: since it takes its food in tiny snacks, the shrew is out and about on the trail day and night, and the constant and penetrating rustling sounds it makes get on the cat's nerves. However, as Roger Tabor points out, carnivorous animals generally like the flavour of herbivores much better than the flavour of other meat-eating animals. Cats discriminate between bird and bird, much as they do between mouse and mouse: while they love songbirds of the finch family, they find thrushes much less appetising. Sparrows who fall victim to the feline hunting instinct are usually left lying as if they were flying shrews.

The wild cousins of the domestic cat can also be very picky about their food, and even develop curious cravings for certain species of prey which can be described only as a quirk or mania. Very likely the reason behind such behaviour is the urge to absorb a certain cocktail of amino acids which are particularly good for the body's protein requirements. Many leopards love to eat dogs, and will greedily devour any domestic dog and if need be any jackal they can find in their hunting range. In the Sudan there is even a legend explaining why the leopard is so fond of eating the cat's traditional enemy. The dog was once employed by the leopard, and was given the job of babysitting the leopard cub. However, he neglected his work, and to this day the cat has sworn revenge. Fearing punishment for his dereliction of duty, the dog took refuge with men, who gave him lodging and protection. But as soon as he leaves human dwellings, retribution threatens. In fact the leopard is something of an opportunist in its eating habits and will consume anything, from dung beetles to ostriches to baboons.

The lynx too will happily turn dogs into cat-food, and this passion was its undoing in the Middle Ages. As more and more land came under the plough, the lynx's natural game preserves in the forests of Europe shrank, and so the hungry animal took to raiding sheep and goats as they grazed. However, its favourite food was sheepdogs. The shepherds complained to the farmers, who in turn complained to the lords of the manor; as rumour spread the attacks gradually assumed the dimension of dreadful acts of terror, and finally the lynxes were trapped and wiped out.

A lion usually pays almost no attention at all to a mouse; it probably guesses that such a tiny meal is not worth the trouble. In ancient Rome lions were trained to amuse the populace by hunting rabbits, catching them, playing with them as a cat plays with a mouse, and finally bringing them back to the animal trainer. Lions in Nairobi National Park feed largely on white-tailed gnu, although these animals make up only about four per cent of the mammalian population and are just as hard to catch as other ungulates such as zebras. The answer to the puzzle is probably that gnu like eating juicy leaves with a high content of valuable proteins; the more easily satisfied zebra, on the other hand, is content to graze on grass of poor quality and probably has a flavour of its own to match. But the difference in flavour presumably makes more demands on the lions: animals which seek out high-quality food, like the gnu, generally have larger brains and are thus cleverer and more difficult to catch than animals which will put up with a poorer but readily available diet.

However, lions are less choosy about their food than any other big cats. They do not even shrink from cannibalism, and will eat their own species: dead cubs or comrades who have died in a fight, of sickness or of old age. The king of the beasts, incidentally, has an inveterate hatred of its smaller cousin the leopard and will kill leopards without mercy; however, lions do not seem to like the taste of their arch-enemies, and will never touch the flesh of a leopard they have killed, perhaps because of the bad amino acids it contains.

The lion, who begins by eating the intestines of its prey, which are full of fat, vitamins and iodine, has another discreditable feeding habit. It is inclined to get at least twenty per cent and at most fifty per cent of its food by stealing from other beasts of prey such as cheetahs, leopards and hyenas. This ruthless trick is reflected in the stories and legends of the Swahili people. In one of their tales, a lion cunningly succeeds in cheating nine hyenas out of ten zebu killed while they were all hunting together. The hyenas are outwitted, and there is nothing whatever left for them.

Cheetahs are fond of eating Thomson's gazelles, which have particularly fastidious eating habits and will greedily stuff themselves with nutritious fruits. Tigers have a special passion for wild pigs. The pigs obviously taste so good that they will even drag frozen corpses out of the snow. The tiger is the mightiest trencherman of all beasts of prey. One of them once devoured a buffalo weighing eight hundred kilograms in just three days; its annual food requirements are about thirty cattle or eighty deer. Finally, of all the big cats the tiger most frequently gets the terrifying reputation of being a man-eater, although in the normal way it seldom attacks humans, who could easily be killed in its hunting district. In exceptional conditions, however, tigers (and lions and leopards) can develop an appetite for Homo sapiens. These are almost always old or injured animals, or tigers driven from their natural habitat who cannot find any other kind of prey. Sometimes the 'perverse' taste may have derived from the chance find of a body which gave the tiger a taste for human flesh. Man-eaters kill only in desperation and infrequently.

There is a precedent: a case in which tigers were conditioned to be man-eaters in the best Pavlovian manner. During the Vietnam war, a macabre but academically interesting phenomenon was discovered: tigers soon came to realise that gunfire (the dinner bell) was regularly associated with food (in the shape of human bodies). Soon they would turn up after every exchange of fire, demanding tribute. The Bengal tiger is the most dangerous of the big cats to man. In 1869 a female of the species in the valley of the Nain in the eastern

Himalayas treated herself to a hundred and twenty-seven human beings in four months. In 1876 four thousand two hundred and eighteen people were killed in India by Bengal tigers, and even in 1979 eighteen Indians came to an untimely end in the jaws of a tiger.

Cats obviously greatly prefer butcher's meat to the stuff of which rats and mice are made. This has been proved by experiments in which cats could choose freely between various basic foods; the American biologist Edward Kane has described them. Rodents clearly taste much nastier than the cat's enthusiasm for hunting them might lead us to suppose. The pet-food industry would probably not make much of a profit from tinned mouse stew or rat-liver flavoured cat-food. Cats would buy beef; it contains better amino acids. This, however, must mean that long before it took that fateful step into domestication on the banks of the Nile, the cat had a palate much too finely adjusted for its ecological niche, a phenomenon which may be described as anticipatory evolution. Small cats simply cannot bring down large cattle. But after all, our own 'wild' ancestors probably had as discriminating a palate as can now appreciate the amazing gourmet creations of top three-star restaurants. One reason why cats do not like carrion is probably the fact that molecules develop in it which have an inhibiting effect on the amino acid sensors.

The second main group of taste cells, as in humans, reacts to a wide spectrum of sour stimuli. Among other things, the sour zones are stimulated by the free fatty acids which the body uses to convey energy and build cell walls. Cats seem to have a strong antipathy to medium-chain fatty acids such as occur in coconut oil. That may account for their frequent dislike of hand-cream and similar products. However, we do not know just what it is they do not like about this type of fatty acid.

The third and last group of taste cells found in a concentration large enough to be worth mentioning is also some way removed from human experience. These sensors respond primarily to nucleotides. Nucleotides are biological molecules which store and transmit energy. Some of the taste sensors do react to bitter stimuli, so that there is some justification for saying that they are sensitive to bitter flavours. However, that is probably not their main function, since receptors of this type are found exclusively in carnivorous species. Many nucleotides, moreover, act as 'flavour enhancers' during the digestion of food. Others again occur in meat which is about to decompose and rot.

A relatively small number of feline taste cells is actually devoted to the perception of water. To modern humans, water is merely one of the main subsidiary components of food, something which tends to get past our chemical sensory apparatus unnoticed. We may be able to taste Perrier, but not ordinary tap water. The idea of water having its own intense flavour puts a severe strain on our imaginations. Evolution, the blind watchmaker, had to overcome considerable technical difficulties to make it possible for an animal to taste water; the ability is one that cat and dog share. The problem is that the taste cells in the mouth are being constantly washed with water in the form of the animal's own saliva, as the American biologist Linda Bartoshuk points out. Chemical receptors which are in uninterrupted contact with the substance stimulating them, however, become dulled and lose sensitivity in that area of perception for which they were designed. That is why most people cannot smell their own odours nearly as well as those of other people. Nature finally managed to solve the problem because saliva always contains a certain concentration of salt. The presence of salt greatly reduces the force of the water sensors. Only when the cat is 'filling up' with water and washing its tongue clean do the relevant sensors become activated. If any salt at all is mixed with a cat's drinking water the receptors concerned will 'play dead'. The cat cannot confuse other drinks with a high water content, such as milk, with the real thing, since such liquids have a higher salt content.

In many ways the cat's world of taste is a strange one, very different from ours, and not just because it can taste certain 'exotic' nuances which correspond to nothing in our own gustatory range. It seems even more curious that certain basic features, things we take as much for granted as daily bread, are conspicuous by their absence in the cat. Its ability to taste salt is obviously extremely underdeveloped. Some of the taste buds which respond to amino acids do have a certain sensitivity to salt, but it is so small, in Bradshaw's opinion, that it may be discounted. This is rather odd, since salty flavours have a very high priority for other mammals. We know that life originated in the sea, and all our body cells are still washed by a fluid which, like the ocean, contains salts in solution (electrolytes). As these minerals are essential to life, most living creatures develop a strong craving for salt if their own stocks run low.

It is quite possible that the cat can afford this 'blind spot' in its chemical sensory world because its diet in a natural environment consists almost exclusively of prey animals, particularly rodents. This high-quality diet contains all the minerals in well-balanced concentration. In other words, if the mouse is not short of salt, neither is the cat. It is different for us humans, since the lords of creation are omnivores, literally 'eaters of everything', who sometimes have to survive for a considerable period on a vegetarian diet. However, as plants contain relatively little salt, omnivores need a good sense of where to get that essential part of the diet. Fleming says that on hot days tigers love to lick the sweat of their human keepers, but we do not know exactly what it is they like about it, since perspiration contains other ingredients as well as the salt that it forms on our skin. Many proteins in solution and other building blocks of body chemistry are also brought to the surface along with glandular excretions. Our own observations of one of our cats, Cujo, leave us in no doubt that he loves licking potato crisps, but here again, we cannot say for certain exactly what it is in the mixture of fat, salt, seasonings and flavour enhancers that arouses his enthusiasm.

We are inclined to make a figurative connection between cats and sugar by saying that cats (and particularly kittens) look 'sweet'. In German, people with a sweet tooth are called *Naschkatzen*, meaning literally 'nibbling cats'. However, such figures of speech are very wide of the truth, since the cat's tongue has remarkably little sense of sweetness. Indeed, it used to be thought that cats could not taste sweet flavours at all, but it now seems that its tongue does have a tiny number of sweetness receptors, although they wake from their trance-like sleep only in the presence of an unusually high concentration of sugar. According to David Taylor the number of these sweetness sensors is increasing as the cat acquires more and more of its human companions' bad habits.

In one experiment, cats with a choice between sweetened and plain water showed no clear preference, while other mammals in the same situation will make straight for the sweetened liquid. A sweet flavour, in nature, is an alluring message that the food contains a form of starch (carbohydrate) which can be rapidly turned into grape sugar (glucose). Glucose is the universal supplier of energy to the body; all cells with work of any kind to do need it. In the cat, this fuel is almost exclusively manufactured by the conversion of amino acids. Unlike human beings, the cat does not have the enzyme ptyalin in its saliva; ptyalin breaks down starch even while it is in the mouth. Cats also have only very small amounts of a certain enzyme (glucokinase) which stems the flood of glucose attacking the organism after a very sugary meal. (Human stomachs, on the other hand, contain fewer of the sharp acids which help to dissolve bones.) As cats cannot 'scent' even quite large amounts of sugar in water, they would carry on regardless until sweet stuff was coming out of their ears.

We can get a rough idea of how sweet things taste to cats by chewing the leaves of silkweed, a plant which temporarily switches off the ability to taste sweetness, making sugar seem insipid and grainy. Conversely, Africans who eat a fruit which they call 'the wonder fruit' temporarily lose their sensitivity to sour flavours. Lemons suddenly taste sweet, and anything which previously had a sour flavour suddenly acquires a soft, sweet aftertaste.

Recent observations, however, show that cats much prefer diluted milk if it has sugar added. The authors' own tests, although they might not come up to the strict methodological requirements of a Nobel Prize committee, produced the same results. Sweet fruit yoghurt and sweet quark were much more popular than plain milk products. 'Lite' varieties containing artificial sweetener instead of sugar obviously tasted just as good as the genuine article. Our experimental subject Hannibal, no mean trencherman anyway, developed such a liking for low-calorie cherry yoghurt that he would dip his paw daintily in the tub and clean the last drops out of it with great expertise. It is a well-known fact that many adult cats lack the enzyme necessary to digest lactose, the milk sugar found in the original diet of all of us. Such animals cannot digest milk and milk products, which give them diarrhoea and inflammation of the bowels. Cats share this problem with many adult humans in Asia, where milk products are regarded as 'unclean'. One may wonder how cats have managed for the last few centuries on farms where they were fed exclusively on milk, or scraps of food in milk.

No doubt people have always noticed that most cats will lap a saucer of milk with obvious enjoyment – even if there are unfortunate consequences later. However, not many will have guessed that the little gourmets are naturally programmed to prefer a 'high-proof' drink. Ordinary full-cream cow's milk with its relatively low fat content of three and a half per cent is too watery for cats; the mother cat's milk has a higher fat content of five per cent. Really thick, creamy cow's

milk from the top of the bottle best answers the cat's craving for cream. Recently, special 'milk for cats' has been marketed by the resourceful pet-food industry: it is based on cow's milk and has the correct biological values.

In any case, cats (and the Chinese) can safely satisfy any wish they may have for milk products more cheaply and without any problems with yoghurt, which more or less digests itself, being full of cultures which turn the indigestible lactose into harmless lactic acids. Yoghurt also has the advantage of enriching the intestinal flora with the bacilli of the lactobacillus family which it contains. They act to form antibiotic active substances in the digestive tract, and these substances combat infections and toxins. Fruit yoghurt, low in fat, is therefore an ideal treat for any sweet-toothed domestic cat, and products described as 'extra light', with a very low fat content, actually derive their sweetness from a 'good' amino acid; this natural sweetener, very popular in the food industry at present, is called aspartame and is also used to sweeten various diet cola drinks. But of course all cats are self-willed individualists, and one will love what another hates.

Murr the cat, in E. T. A. Hoffmann's novel, gets a saucer of sweetened cream now and then as a sign of approval. The fact that cats prefer sweetened milk does not, however, necessarily mean that they have developed a sweet tooth, Bradshaw points out. Perhaps milk develops an entirely different aroma or texture when sweetener is added. Or perhaps the reason is that milk contains a certain amount of salt which deadens the water sensors, as described above. It is thought that the cat's water sensors entirely suppress its ability to taste sugar. In that case the sweet taste could develop unchecked only in milk (or in slightly salted water). The ingenious strategies employed by cat-food manufacturers do not make matters any clearer. The brand leader adds a little caramel to its most expensive product (the one in the rectangular foil tray). Caramel is a brownish-yellow sugar heated to the point where it becomes a sticky substance much used in confectionery. Again, one wonders whether cats really like the sweet taste or whether the scent of caramel does nothing but rise to their nostrils. One way or another the question of whether cats can have a sweet tooth must remain open for the present, particularly as some of their large wild relatives evidently do like sweet things. Manchurian tigers, for instance, like to eat sweet walnuts in autumn (shells and all) and their Malaysian cousins love the sweet fruit of the durian.

In fact there are many indications that the organism can develop a voracious appetite for foods outside the range of its own sense of taste. For instance, mammals often display an 'animal' craving for those natural products which will compensate for deficiencies in the diet. Because of this, it has long been suspected that a built-in 'body wisdom' guides the appetite towards what will provide it with the substances necessary for life. Many of these substances – for instance, vitamins – are present in food in such low dosages that no receptor, however finely tuned, can register them. Yet the sailors of the past, afflicted by scurvy, must have felt a natural longing for the lemons containing Vitamin C which would cure the disease.

A good example of body wisdom is provided by common

salt. Many wild animals will go on long pilgrimages to a salt lick very far away when their electrolytes are running low. A case has even been recorded in which a small boy with an adrenal disorder spontaneously developed a craving for salt and thus saved his own life. Obviously, a salt deficiency will immediately increase the euphoria felt in consuming it, which may explain the tiger's liking for human sweat. In any case, the same principle functions with nutrients which the organism cannot taste at all, such as Vitamin B1 (thiamine), as experiments with rodents suffering from thiamine deficiency have shown. The animals were given a choice of several dishes, one of which tasted of vanilla and contained a good slug of Vitamin B1. They very quickly understood that it was good for them, and on later occasions immediately switched to the vanilla-flavoured diet when they were running short of thiamine.

Body wisdom can make many cats show a liking for sugar, as the example of the cheetah shows. Cheetahs are thorough-bred racing cats, and with a top speed of over a hundred and twenty kilometres an hour they easily outstrip all other land mammals. They need that turn of speed, since they are competing for food with other big cats like lions and leopards. Cheetahs hunt in the heat of the mid-day sun, when lions are lounging about under the trees. After a few hundred metres its strenuous biomechanical performance heats the cheetah's blood to a temperature of forty and a half degrees, endangering the nervous system. However, the cheetah can keep its sprint up for only half a kilometre; once it has made its kill it drops to the ground, exhausted. At this point lions often ruthlessly seize their opportunity and steal the food.

When the cheetah eats it gorges first on the blood and liver of its prey. These are precisely those parts of the body which have the highest sugar content. In fact the liver is a kind of silo, storing sugar in the form of glycogen. The glycogen can be used directly to deliver muscular energy, and that quality must appeal to the cheetah even if it is unable to taste actual sweetness. In a way liver is the counterpart of the chocolate bar which top athletes consume during competition to keep their glucose levels up, and the blood of the prey is the counterpart of those 'isotonic' drinks which have become so popular in recent years. Both fitness boosters contain the correct concentrations of salts and mineral substances.

There is also another phenomenon which might explain why cat species like liver so much. The light-sensitive pigments in the rods of the retina, also called visual purple or rhodopsin, are based on the carotenoid family of molecules. This basic substance, which is red or yellow in colour, has a significance for animals similar to that of chlorophyll in the plant world. As animals cannot synthesise carotenoids for themselves, they have to absorb them in plant foods. Inside the body, they are converted to vitamin A, which helps the retina to take in light. However, as the cat's diet in its evolutionary past consisted exclusively of meat, it forfeited its ability to convert carotenoids into photopigments. It has to consume the vitamin in its converted state, and vitamin A is found in very high concentrations in fresh liver.

Vitamin A deficiency soon gives rise to problems such as photophobia, decreased vision in dim light, or night blindness. Rabbits (and humans) can easily make up for any such deficiency by eating carrots and other red and yellow vegetables. Cats, on the other hand, depend on getting the vitamin from liver (and tinned cat-food). Interestingly, the ancient Egyptians were the first to discover that you can cure night blindness by eating liver. Perhaps their sacred cats told them. Later, the cod-liver oil disliked by children played an important part in supplying vitamin A in winter. Finally, the consumption of carotenoids has recently attained cult status; the theory is that they can capture toxic metabolic products (free radicals) and thus help to prevent ageing and cancer.

The cat has taken to a more comfortable life-style since its domestication, one which should make the need for surges of power delivered by sugar superfluous. However, the tiger on the hearth shares a liking for fresh liver with its fleet-footed relative the cheetah, and we may well wonder whether a wish for rapid access to energy is behind it. Surprisingly, the high sugar content of liver does not give the cat any digestive problems, even if it positively gorges itself on the stuff. The pet-food industry also adds a certain amount of starch to its products so that the cat need not divert any calorific value from the protein it requires for other physical functions and cell regeneration. Cats who have lost weight and are suffering from lack of appetite can be pepped up with boviserin, a serum made from the blood of cattle.

In the secret occult writings of the Middle Ages, incidentally, there was a common belief that witches had an additional, third nipple. This nipple was supposed to provide not milk but blood, and the witch used it to suckle her familiar, the black cat, says Fred Gettings in a book on esotericism. During the Inquisition, women suspected of witchcraft were promptly given a thorough body search which included a feverish hunt for any pimple that might be interpreted as the nipple for the cat. On the other hand, those women who thought they actually were witches made their infamous ointments with cat's blood, among other ingredients. They presumably hoped to acquire the cat's magic powers and nine lives in this way. Because of the cat's legendary fertility, it was thought in Arab countries that drinking its blood would make men irresistible, a superstition which cost many cats their lives. And although black cats were suspected in the Dark Ages of sinister connections with hell and black magic, their livers were frequently used in the rituals of exorcism employed to cast out devils. Presumably people were thinking along homoeopathic lines: evil would be best driven out with evil.

Further evidence of the domestic cat's body wisdom is provided by a piece of feline conduct which many cat owners write off as just an odd habit. All cats will sometimes nibble blades of grass, and if there is no lawn available they will vandalise your house plants. The usual explanation is that cats use the grass as an emetic to get rid of the troublesome hairballs they have accumulated while grooming themselves. Other experts think that a salad of grass provides the body with roughage when there is a corresponding lack of it. But as Desmond Morris sensibly points out, the cat usually just picks at this rabbit-food, consuming far less than one would expect if the grass were eaten to act as roughage. More probably, the cat is getting vitamins or valuable substances of some kind which are absent from a meat diet, and which do their job even in tiny doses. Morris believes the substance concerned is folic acid, a water-soluble vitamin essential for the production of haemoglobin, the iron-containing red pigment in the blood. Lack of folic acid can restrict growth and make the cat anaemic.

This interpretation also seems probable because all the wild relations of our domestic cats pick at vegetables, fruits and greenery now and then, as Wilfried Meyer, a veterinarian from Hanover, points out. The European wild-cat occasionally eats leaves and rowan berries, the Bengal cat feasts on tree fungi now and then, and the flat-headed cat even digs up sweet potatoes with obvious pleasure. Large quantities of grapes have been found in the stomach of the caracal, a distant relative of the puma. The serval sometimes nibbles bananas and avocados, and the tiger likes to season its menu with a vitamin-rich dose of sea buckthorn, woodland berries and pine-nuts.

Such observations belong to a chapter in our understanding of the animal kingdom opened only in the last few years by ethopharmaceutical studies. Many animals help themselves from 'God's own pharmacy' with surprising expertise, and cure indispositions and deficiencies with all kinds of natural remedies. Wild chimpanzees eat certain rare leaves and shrubs containing anti-bacterial substances to cure intestinal disorders. They merely lick the leaves instead of chewing them, to avoid unwanted admixtures in the stomach. Their pilgrimage to find medicinal plants does not take place until evening, when the active substance in the plant reaches its highest concentration. During the dry period, zebras and gnu display curious behaviour: they lick hard at termite mounds and the ground around them, because when they built their home the termites brought valuable vital substances such as sodium and calcium up from underground to the light of day. As the natural diet of ungulates has been practically exhausted in the drought, this is useful nourishment. We may suppose that the members of the cat family also practise this form of self-medication, since it would enhance the flavour of their prey.

But even body wisdom sometimes makes bad mistakes. Every year a number of cats – just how many it is difficult to estimate – go to grass, as one might say, because they have eaten a poisonous plant such as philodendron. Nine lives are not always enough for a cat to learn the difference between 'good' and 'bad' plants. The odour, the plant structure and the bright colours obviously prove irresistible much of the time. Fleming recommends painting Tabasco on plants which are bad for cats, to deliver a fiery sensation through the trigeminal system and spoil the cat's appetite. Incidentally, a cat confined to living indoors will take it kindly if you lay out a little garden for it in a bowl, containing plants and herbs like thyme, parsley, grass, etc., and to give your pet a nice trip, you could plant catmint too.

Committed vegetarians spreading the gospel of a meatless life-style often cite a line of argument deriving from nutritional ecology. This argument considers it irresponsible to squander large quantities of plant energy on raising a precisely defined quantity of meat. It would be much more rational and ecological, say the vegetarians, to derive the same nutritional value straight from the vegetable kingdom in the form of soya, tofu and high-protein cereals. The cat will not win any brownie points here, let alone greenie ones. It was once worked out that an adult vole which contributes just about forty grams to a hungry cat's dinner must have eaten at least ten kilograms of grass and other vegetable food before performing this unselfish act. A mouse, however – according to data provided by Ulrich Klever, both chef and cat expert – accounts for a mere hundred and twenty kilojoules. This means that an 'organically' fed cat would have to eat about ten mice a day to stay in good condition. Thirty-six tons of vegetable biomass would therefore have to be devoted to the feeding of a single cat.

Recently scientists have made careful calculations of the amount of biomass consumed annually by cats both large and small – biomass meaning the percentage of their typical prey animals. The big cats (lions, cheetahs, leopards, jaguars and pumas) get their claws on about ten per cent of the prey in their area. The small cats do a great deal better. The ocelot accounts for some seventy-five per cent of available prey animals. The difference is connected with hunting behaviour. Small cats satisfy their nutritional needs with prey animals which are very much smaller, even in relation to their own body size. Moreover, the metabolism of small animals works at top speed, like a highly tuned racing car; consequently, they always need more food. And they can get it without disturbing the ecological balance. The animals they hunt multiply like the proverbial rabbits which they frequently are, and so the gap is always being filled. Big cats, on the other hand, are always hunting huge mountains of meat, and can afford to go on the trail only once or twice a week.

Since cats are so frequently mentioned in connection with the term 'carnivore', it is easy for misunderstandings to arise. Why, one may wonder, do we not go all the way and give these beasts of prey what they really like best – steak, mince or fresh liver? The fact is, however, that cats are not exactly carnivores, meat-eaters, in the strict sense of the word, but eaters of prey animals; in the wild they will eat the entire body of their prey, hide, hair and all. In such a context, as Andrew Kitchener points out, it is mere wishful thinking to suppose that feline species purposely hunt weak and sickly prey and thus act as a kind of health police. Hunters from the illustrious ranks of the Felidae differ from most other beasts of prey in their hunting technique, which consists of stalking followed by a swift pounce, and will lay low perfectly healthy animals. The dog family, on the other hand, really does sift the chaff from the wheat in its extended hunting expeditions.

Small rodents are the easiest to eat, and are devoured from the head downwards. Many beasts of prey eat the half-digested stomach contents of their vegetarian kill as a kind of starter; when this happens, as Michael W. Fox humorously points out, the vegetables come before the main course. But the main course itself does not consist solely of meat, since it also contains the animal's skin, entrails, brain and other special titbits. Dessert consists chiefly of the bones, nibbled instead of nuts or fruit because they contain calcium, which is necessary to support life. Many cats neatly remove the gall bladder and bowels before eating their prey, but others are too greedy for good table manners of this kind. If the prey animal's fur is eaten it will be vomited up later. Cats often pluck small birds before eating them, at least until their patience runs out.

The cat will take a short walk before settling down to eat its fill. It is thought that this is a way of working off the remains of the tension which built up during the hunt. Given this opportunity, mice who have been playing dead will often surreptitiously leave the table. Because of their specialised jaw structure, cats do not generally chew, but cut their food up into strips or small chunks with their carnassials, which act as knives. While the cat is doing this its head is at a slight sideways angle to its prey, showing what hard work cutting up meat is. The harder the flesh of the mouse, the further the head is turned to one side. If the prey is particularly tough the cat will lay its ears back. It consumes its food standing or crouching, changing the side on which it is eating from time to time.

Since cats in the wild eat the whole of their prey, they are getting what is in effect a perfectly balanced diet containing all the necessary nutrients and anabolic substances. For instance, meat on its own contains very little calcium but a good deal of phosphorus, and in the long term a cat's bones will suffer if it is fed on nothing but meat. Raw meat and entrails, indeed, frequently contain bacteria and harmful active substances. Finally, a raw diet is better for a four-legged hunter who needs to stay fit, on account of the composition of the basic nutrients it contains. The dinner of a cat living wild is only seven to twelve per cent fat. A piece of sausage, on the other hand, can easily contain up to forty or fifty per cent fat. You are literally loving your cat to death if you feed it only butcher's meat. Again, plant protein lacks many important amino acids essential for the cat's health and general well-being; it is cruel to try keeping a cat on a vegetarian diet. In time, cats who do not get enough protein in their food become bad-tempered and hyper-aggressive. Meat proteins contain the amino acid tryptophan, which is converted into the neurotransmitter serotonin. Serotonin is necessary to dull pain and calm moods of agitation. Human beings with a serotonin deficiency commit suicide and violent crimes more frequently. It is even thought now that a diet very low in cholesterol may reduce the serotonin level; even a 'healthy' diet, therefore, can have distinctly unhealthy consequences. So far no observations have been made of cats in this context, but monkeys kept on a low-cholesterol diet became very aggressive and attacked their companions angrily.

Tinned cat-food and dry cat-food, like prey animals, contain a well-balanced mixture of all the important nutrients. These days most pet-food manufacturers observe the strict criteria of the American National Research Council (or NRC). They satisfy the cat's appetite for meat with pieces of beef, pork, lamb, game, poultry, and such by-products of butchery as heart, lungs and rumen. Standard types of cat-food are one-third meat 'stretched' with two-thirds vegetables, cereal and similar fillers; premium brands, however, contain twice as much meat, according to the American nutritionist Glenn Brown. However, even tins claiming to contain pure meat have a ten per cent carbohydrate content.

The actual 'meat' consists of 'superfluous materials now less in demand because of modern eating habits', according to the discreet wording of a leaflet from the pet-food manufacturing brand leaders. For instance, the remains of deep-sea fish left over after the preparation of fish fillets may be added. Precise information is hard to come by, but according to Glenn Brown and other writers, cat-food may also contain less attractive items such as chicken feet. A large proportion, however, usually consists of the entrails of large animals, for instance the intestines of cattle and sheep, pigs' stomachs, and other items of offal that turn many people's stomachs such as the spleen, kidneys, lungs, udder, etc.

In addition, as the American expert James E. Coburn tells us, cat-food contains damaged or unattractive-looking eggs and other by-products of chicken farming. Cattle who are poorly, handicapped, sick, dying or dead will be culled, and if their constitution was not in too bad a way, then they can be processed for pet-food – at least in the USA. However, that vital fluid blood is surprisingly seldom mixed with the other ingredients; it would detract so much from the look of the tin's contents that pet-owners might not like it. Or perhaps, says Coburn, blood is too expensive, since it can be used and is needed for other purposes.

The inventiveness employed by pet-food manufacturers to make money from rejected materials is evident in a patent taken out by a British firm, which received the critical attention of the German news magazine *Der Spiegel* a little while ago. The document, said the news report, 'concerns a manner of processing food so as to give a fibrous appearance resembling meat fibres'. The list of ingredients showed that the meat was not exactly prime steak but offal, meat by-products, gluten, defatted soya flour, soya concentrates, dried blood, skin, fishmeal and various other things. However, it would be wrong to apply human notions of a proper diet to pet-food; for instance, chicken feet are very good for cats because of their high calcium and phosphorus content.

Moreover, dogs and cats are very fond of certain things to eat which seem disgusting to human senses (and the human imagination), as Fox points out. Their chemical sensory apparatus is very different from ours, and they can 'smell' whether food is good for them without eating any of it at all. In this they are like wine experts who only have to sniff a wine to say whether it is a fine vintage or not. All things considered, anyway, it would be inadvisable to pick an argument about taste with a hungry tiger.

One should be careful, in any case, not to feed domestic cats solely on ready-prepared food with a tuna fish base over a long period. Recently, a team led by the American physiologist Katherine A. Houpt gave its purring 'guinea pigs' a monotonous diet of this kind over a period of some months. As a result, the cats stopped purring! They became less active, quieter, and spent longer stretched motionless on the floor than the control group which was eating a normal diet. The symptoms probably arose because tuna fish has a relatively high mercury content, and mercury is a neurotoxin. Apart from that, a diet of fish alone would have another unpleasant side effect: many cats fed on nothing but fish have a strong smell. Being the proud and sensitive creatures they are, they hate to have people sniff pointedly in their presence. In fact an old Italian fresco shows the mortal sin of vanity symbolised by a cat standing in a small and inconspicuous position at the edge of the picture.

It should be mentioned that a consumer test carried out in 1989 gave beef-based cat-food toxicological clearance. Its content of harmful substances was so low as to be negligible, and the concentration of nutrients was within the legally prescribed bounds, even in the cheaper brands. In Germany, where this test took place, there are statutory regulations

applying to the manufacture of pet-food, some of them more rigorous than the regulations covering food for human consumption.

For sales reasons, the cat-food manufacturers have already tailored their product to appeal to human feelings, just as the packaging of children's toys appeals to adult motivation. The sharp aroma which once used to rise to the nose when you opened the cat's tin was the result of the mysterious 'dressing' which pervaded the anonymous mixture. This olfactory substance, known by the brand name of 'Digest', is made from pieces of meat predigested in tanks by enzymes, as the journalist Penny Moser discovered during her research into the American pet-food industry. The basis of the substance consists primarily of the internal organs of fish and poultry subjected to the process of autolysis in the tanks. Autolysis is a kind of self-digestion which takes place in an entirely sterile way, i.e., in the absence of bacteria, when enzymes emerge from dying cells and decompose the tissues. The enzymes break down meat fibres to the desired consistency. Phosphoric acid is added at a certain point to stop fermentation and keep the 'Digest' from decaying. Bacteria do not like this acid environment, but the tongue does: phosphoric acid is used as an acidifier in many cola drinks.

The finished product is even baked into dried food, since cats obviously like the smell of it. In this they are just like humans, who also like certain predigested products (such as ripe cheese) if fermentation is well advanced and can be identified by a noticeable 'bloom'. The dressing, which may be up to ten per cent of the entire weight, is often sprayed mechanically on to the pressed cat-food. The American veterinarian James G. Morris thinks that its addition probably makes the food more palatable to the cat because it extracts amino acids, their protein chains or peptides, and free fatty acids from the tissue, as one might extract ore from a mine. This industrial pre-treatment provides the palate with quasi-pure stimulation in tune with its most secret desires. Perhaps the same mechanism may even explain the human liking for cheese, yoghurt, quark and other pre-digested milk and delicatessen products. The improvement in terms of taste, at least, can be quantitatively assessed: American researchers have calculated that the addition of 'Digest' heightens the appeal of cat-food to its target public two or three times over, according to the veterinarian Tony Buffington.

As chance will have it, wasps obviously have a great liking for the same food. At the time of writing, New Zealand has a major wasp problem and seems to be solving it very successfully with poisoned cat-food. The aggressive flying insects were accidentally introduced from Europe a few decades ago, and are now threatening the natural environment. To the wasps, New Zealand is a land of unlimited opportunity because they have no natural enemies there. After extensive experiments, it turned out that only cat-food would work as bait. Dosed with the right poison, it reduces plagues of wasps by ninety per cent within ten days, while the friendly bees ignore the traps and come to no harm. No wonder: bees, being sweet-toothed vegetarians, feed on nectar, while wasps are flying marauders and feed their larvae in particular on a mush of chewed and squashed insects. Incidentally, they are also very fond of liver. In the summer, cat owners are often irritated to see wasps falling on

the cat's full bowl and tainting its contents with excretions which obviously put the cat right off its food.

These days smells of cream or gravy frequently rise to our noses as we open a tin for our pet. The sharp smell of 'Digest' has now been muted by more delicate aromas and essences. Some of the ingredients, however, definitely aim to appeal to the feline palate, and are designed to make the mushy product tastier and more attractive to it. 'Seasonings' like fish, garlic or caramel are intended to keep the four-legged consumers up to the mark, says Fox. According to the British writer Jeremy Cherfas, the industry has made extensive attempts to make cat-food even more tempting to its ultimate consumer by adding catmint. He was told by one researcher, with some disappointment, that the catmint was no good at enticing cats to eat; history does not relate whether the experimental animals rubbed their heads blissfully in their scented food instead.

If you are cooking for your pets yourself, you should remember that human seasonings such as pepper and paprika are unsuitable for cats. As they like substantial, nourishing food, the meat can sometimes have onions, celery, carrots and similar vegetables added. It is also worth trying them with herbal products such as aniseed, fennel or herbal teas, but the fastidious feeder's individual taste will always play a major part in its diet.

As for choosing cat's meat, the guidelines of human tastes are not always appropriate. Cats eat horsemeat with obvious enjoyment. It is a lean meat, and thus good for their figures. Brains are very suitable too, particularly for young cats, since they contain many valuable amino acids. Game is extremely popular with cats, and they love pigeons. Fish, particularly herrings, are the favourite food of many cats, and they may like smoked fish too.

Some well-intentioned cat books recommend complementing the diet of our domesticated marauders with the occasional addition of the complete bodies of prey animals: mice, rats, rabbits, pigeons, ducks, chickens. However, it is doubtful whether this 'biological' diet really corresponds to the cat's notion of a three-star menu. After all, cats did not attach themselves to the ancient Egyptians in order to be fobbed off with ordinary raw food from the woods and meadows (without any added dressing). If there is beef or lamb cooking, a whole bouquet of over a thousand scent and flavour molecules is liberated. No raw body or freshly killed game provides that, and the same fact also sets limits to the mass spread of vegetarianism. Indeed, perhaps it actually explains the puzzle of the cat's self-domestication. At least one thing is certain: cats instantly wake from the deepest of slumbers if the fragrance of grilling, roasting or barbecued meat reaches their nostrils.

In the pet-food industry, anyway, highly paid nutritionists are constantly developing new recipes, which are kept strictly secret. The leading European cat-food manufacturers were similarly unforthcoming in answer to questions, giving the authors only a few general comments about their 'nouvelle cuisine' for cats: 'The flavour of our cat-food products derives from the choice and mixture of various raw materials . . . Different products may have very different flavourings added.' Even the Pentagon would provide more information about the construction of its secret new bomber. And it would be surprising if European cats were offered recipes quite different from those given to pampered pets in the land of opportunity. 'Food designers' have proved very effective; cats offered various pieces of meat either on their own or with a sauce always preferred the fancier variety. Given the right sauce, perhaps they could even be induced to eat shrews with relish.

Because of their well-developed palate for proteins, cats can probably taste the slightest changes in their food affecting, for instance, the freshness of the meat or the nutritional condition of the fattened animals at slaughter. Bruce Fogle observed that the cats brought to his surgery displayed a passion for a certain brand of rabbit-flavoured cat food. Inquiries sent to the manufacturer elicited a remarkable explanation. While competing brands used farm-bred rabbits to flavour their cat-food, this particular firm had put wild rabbits caught in China into its tins. Since wild prey, in its last moments of life, is flooded with the adrenalin that gives creatures being hunted to death greater speed, the wild rabbits must have had a certain extra flavour.

For similar reasons, when a 'meat mountain' is going cheap anywhere, according to Moser, the bosses of the American pet-food industry will have a few samples flown in. A feline stand-by service, roused if necessary from its digestive slumbers, sets about flavour testing at once, while a whole factory halts its machinery until the tasters have delivered their verdict. The idea conjures up a horrible and indeed barbaric vision of some hypothetical pet-food manufacturer driven by greed for gain making rabbits and other small animals run for their lives in a long-drawn-out process of torment, to give them the right seasoning of mortal terror, stress hormones and adrenalin. Another disquieting thought also springs to mind: perhaps the hypocritical cat plays its cruel game with the prey it only half-heartedly pursues with the unpleasant idea of spicing up its next meal with the natural flavour enhancers of panic and terror.

This idea is perhaps less far-fetched than one might think. In Patrick Süskind's novel *Perfume*, the protagonist, who lives in eighteenth-century Paris, can tell from the smell of his daily glass of milk what mood the cow was in when she was milked. And in the eighteenth century certain strange and repellent culinary customs really did develop in England when bored city dwellers began taking an interest in sadism and witchcraft. A notion was put forward that the flesh of tortured animals tasted better and was good for you. Soon a number of people were following this macabre fashion, and the kitchen became a mixture of slaughterhouse and torture chamber. Live fish were hacked to bits, oxen tortured, pigs and calves beaten to death with knotted ropes, poultry hung up by their feet and slowly bled to death, and animals were flayed alive. All this was done under the impression that the flavour of meat could be improved if the poor creature providing it had suffered the torments of hell first.

In Korea, where dogs have been eaten for over a hundred thousand years, the way in which they are slaughtered is still regarded as determining their flavour. The idea is that if they are hung up alive and beaten, fear and pain enter the bloodstream and proceed to the flesh; only then will it be tender and have a stimulating effect as an aphrodisiac. History does not relate whether cats have ever eaten a morsel

151

of this sadistically flavour-enhanced food, and if so, what they thought of such abuse of their ancient rivals.

In many epochs of history, and in many parts of the world, however, people have preferred to eat cat, and sometimes still do. Cut up and added to soup, it is supposed to help with digestive problems in Vietnam. In China cats are regarded as a delicacy, and in Jamaica they are actually roasted with chopped rat stuffing. Even the Egyptians, who regarded the cat as sacred, probably committed the sacrilege of eating the object of their worship in lean years and periods of drought. It would not be surprising, since they treated even the hedgehog as a delicacy. On old German menus the flesh of Chartreux cats was offered under the euphemism of 'Dachshund'. Medieval German medical treatises recommended the meat of cats as a remedy for vertigo.

It is unlikely that cats were ever front runners in the menu stakes, since in general carnivores do not like the amino acids in the flesh of other carnivores. However, the exception confirms the rule, and cats have sometimes been in their greatest danger from cannibalism in their own ranks. Tigers, for instance, sometimes eat other carnivores and show a particular liking for small cat species, including our own domestic cat. It is said that leopards too occasionally satisfy their hunger with a similar snack.

The pet-food industry of Western Europe is in a curious ideological quandary where it can hardly do anything right. If it uses parts of animals which are unappetising to humans, then sooner or later indignation about its use of rubbishy products will be expressed in the media. But if it were to use top-quality meat, the same media would object to its lack of sensitivity to the plight of starving children around the world. It is often said in the press, particularly around Christmas time, that the rich states are making pet-food out of nutrients and valuable foods which could save millions of human lives in the Third World. Professor Dennis Turner of Zürich points out several inaccuracies in this argument: for one thing, pets are not a luxury, since they provide a better quality of life for their owners than other and more dispensable things like expensive clothes, cars and glossy magazines criticising society. Indeed, pets are kept even in 'poor' countries for that very reason, although in far less comfortable conditions. Furthermore, the contents of pet-food tins are not of a quality to make them fit for human consumption, and the industry provides a chance of making fuller use of the meat we produce. Cries of outrage about this flourishing commercial business have not yet actually benefited the starving peoples of the Third World. Professor Turner feels that it makes no difference what parts of an animal carcase are used to make pet-food so long as it is suitable for an animal diet – and cats like the taste of it.

Regular as clockwork, the mass media also bombard us with moving shock-horror reports of poverty-stricken pensioners in our own Western countries who eat pet-food because they cannot afford a proper diet. These stories often come adorned with highly-coloured – and romantic – sociological connotations, but there is probably little in them.

At first glance the pensioners' desperate act, as described, seems reasonable enough; in principle, cat-food is suitable for human consumption. But closer examination leaves room for considerable doubt. A standard-sized tin of cat-food costs no more than similarly sized tins of cheap but nutritional human food (ravioli, tinned peas, beans, etc.), which can in fact be bought for less in discount stores. What the unfortunate if imaginary pensioners really needed was access to a good consumers' advice bureau. But anyone who is really so down and out that he goes to the pet-food shelves in the supermarket should look in the dog-food section, like Mad Max in the film of that name. Tinned dog-food, with its high carbohydrate and low protein content, is closer to today's recommended human diet.

Presumably the only people who have really sampled cat-food are the sales representatives of the big pet-food firms. In the past the current brand leader, quite a small-scale operation a few decades ago, had to combat the prejudices of small shopkeepers who did not want to sell a full range of cat-food for fear that the rest of their stock might be regarded as suspect. It was no coincidence that around this time many exotic new restaurants fell under the monstrous suspicion of serving their customers pet-food, and quantities of empty tins put out for the dustmen reinforced such notions. If the myths are to be believed, the staunch sales representatives of the period boldly brought out their tin openers and made short work of the image problem before the shopkeepers' very eyes. The rest is history. The business concerned, a branch of the firm which also sells Mars bars, has a huge turnover from dog-food and cat-food today (including the Chappie, Whiskas and Kitekat brands) and takes a very large percentage of the market. Its profits are far from looking like something the cat brought in, except in the literal sense.

The superb service we human tin-openers provide, however, means that more and more cats these days are blowing up to the size of balloons. According to an article in one cat magazine, some ten per cent of cats are overweight. However, standards of corpulence depend very much on the criterion employed: do we go by the grenadier standard or the pygmy norm? Extreme assessments put the number of overweight cats at forty per cent, which incidentally would correspond quite closely to the state of affairs among humans. A recent survey showed that in Western Europe forty-seven per cent of women and thirty-nine per cent of men were overweight. In the cat world too, females are more apt to lose their figures than males. An average cat weighs between three and five kilos; the fattest cat ever recorded weighed twenty-one kilos and had a stomach measurement of seventy-six centimetres. Increased girth puts a strain on the circulation and the skeletal system, but it looks as if cats suffer less from the unhealthy consequences of overweight than other mammals. Cats are cut out for the sybaritic life. And they are ready to indulge themselves at almost any time; this may be to do with the fact that they have short intestines, as mentioned above, and so they must always be 'filling up' in the natural state and need plenty of cat litter in a human household.

The factors that make cats plump are the same as those that cause their owners to burst their seams. The tendency to put on weight is a genetic inheritance passed down to us (and to cats) by our primeval ancestors. Since the amount of food available varies greatly in natural circumstances, evolution has laid down rolls of fat around the belly and hips to store up calories in times of plenty, ready to serve as iron rations in lean times. The body's stores are made of fat because that substance has the highest calorific value. Fatty tissue has a remarkable absorptive capacity. Its building blocks, the fat cells, can swell to ten times their normal size. If necessary they will even produce offshoots of themselves which never go away again. Overweight people have two or three times the normal number of fat cells, and those cells in turn are two or three times the normal size.

These days many people (and cats) live in an industrialised land of milk and honey where they are constantly tempted by culinary pleasures. However, most individuals are able to keep to their proper weight, even when an improved diet is available. It is even thought that all mammals have a given weight, or set point, determined by their heredity and programmed into them, and that the body defends this set point by every possible means. Cats who had a higher fat content than usual smuggled into their food immediately reacted by eating less, so that the calorific value they were absorbing remained the same. Most human beings keep their weight stable over a very long period. According to recent surveys, women put on only eleven kilos on average between the ages of twenty-five and sixty-five; that may sound quite a lot, but it means that the daily 'gain' is only three hundred and fifty milligrams. The extra weight is built up gradually, and a daily extra dose of one per cent more energy will lead to twenty-five per cent extra weight after seven years.

However, the main cause of obesity does not seem to be greed. Most fat people and fat cats do not eat any more than their colleagues whose weight is normal, and are just as physically active. There are indications that the majority of overweight people have a metabolism – the process whereby food is converted into energy and heat – which burns on a lower flame. Those affected 'do well' on less food, burning up less energy and thus getting twice as much from every calorie. This double-edged advantage could never make itself uncomfortably obvious in nature, when there would always be involuntary periods of fasting to consume all the stored fat.

The tendency to obesity seems to be largely inborn, as shown, for instance, by studies of identical twins who have the same genetic inheritance but are brought up in different environments. Such twins usually turn out to weigh the same. But in cats the influence of their human environment also plays a certain part. An owner who is always giving a cat tasty calorific treats like sausage and similar foodstuffs need not be surprised if the cat exceeds its set point sooner or later. Cats too can be quick to develop a liking for junk food, something that will undermine body wisdom and all natural safeguards. The only practical treatment for feline obesity is to reduce the cat's daily diet by thirty to forty per cent; a drastic starvation diet is dangerous and could easily harm the animal's health.

For some time, however, calorie-reduced 'light' products for cats and dogs have been available; the main point of them is that part of their fat content has been removed. Such slimming foods, which contain only two-thirds to one half of the normal calorific value, were initially obtainable only on prescription from a vet, but they are now on the open market in the United Kingdom. Their advantage lies in the fact that they contain a precisely measured amount of vitamins and vital substances, and the dose is easily administered.

However, the crucial criterion, as the Viennese veterinarian Josef Leibetseder points out, is whether or not the actual consumer accepts them. If it does, then one can embark on a slimming programme. As it is a statistical fact that plump owners tend to have plump pets, Leibetseder suggests that the end result is a curious one: both parties compete in shedding the excess pounds!

What began as a quiet little love affair in ancient Egypt has long since become a mass movement – with a huge commercial market for tinned food involved. However, we should not think that the relationship between humans and cats can be reduced to the pampering of a free-loading animal by a generous if hypnotised owner. The American biologist John A. Cavallo supports the theory that *Homo sapiens* owes his present position solely to the theft of food from cat species. Most theories about human evolution conclude that great strides in development first began when there was plenty of high-quality meat protein available. And indeed, the remains of gnu, gazelles and other prey animals have been excavated from the camping sites of early hominids. Because of the many dangers involved in active hunting, our distant ancestors may have stolen the prey of big cats. Their best source would have been leopards, who are good climbers and usually store their prey in tree-tops for safety. However, such tactics would work against lions and cheetahs, but would not deter that excellent climber *Homo habilis*.

There are several indications that this really was the case. Among other things, the usual prey of leopards corresponds in size to the finds at the hominids' camping sites. Moreover, it is particularly easy to get on the track of leopards, who like to store their provisions in small areas near rivers. Finally, researchers have recently observed baboons helping themselves to the stores of nocturnally active leopards. In a certain way, as we all know, human beings are just highly developed baboons. There are some indications that many hominids paid for their thieving inclinations with their lives when a leopard came back to its larder early with a grumbling stomach. If this scenario is accurate, then human provision for domestic cats is only a collective form of compensation. We are merely giving back to our small tame cats what we once took from the big wild ones. And any amount of interest has accumulated since then.

Comments by Francis

Well, something worth knowing at last: hard facts showing due respect for our complex palates and recognising us as the true gourmets of the world. Also certain information which was wholly unknown to me before. I can say, with some justification, that my general knowledge is almost flawless. However, should it prove to have the occasional gap in it, as here, I am modest enough to say so publicly. The fact is, I really had no idea that some cat-food manufacturers employ a staff of tasters of my own kind to assess their products. And very useful too, I'm sure, but I do wonder whether those manufacturers have picked the right cats to do the tasting. It is no secret, after all, that many members of the noble family of Felidae have an unfortunate taste for the high life and will stuff themselves with anything set before them. Observing that the taster eats the meat in bowl A first and then goes on to demolish the contents of bowl B tells us nothing, since he'd probably tuck into both bowls anyway, a

fact which detracts from and indeed entirely distorts the results of the experiments. The Lucullan consequences of such incorrectly conducted investigations could prove fatal. When this brilliant flash of inspiration came to me, I forced myself to make a decision which is mine alone. It will probably cost me much that is dear to my heart, but there are times when one must overcome one's baser instincts and make a sacrifice for the general good. In short, I place myself at the disposal of the institutions concerned as a taster. I know my decision will cause an outcry among my loyal fans, involving as it does great peril of body and soul. The strain on the palate at any time of day or night, the stress caused to the stomach by various meats of unknown origin, and finally the heavy responsibility of which I must always be aware, all these will certainly challenge my constitution. Indeed, I do not yet know if I can ever master the task. To lighten the burden a little, I imagine I will be given a suitable environment in which to carry out the tests, let's say a French chalet. Furthermore, the experimental meals should be cooked and served by a master of his craft, a five-star chef from the Mediterranean countries, and of course I shall have to study his references very thoroughly first. I am in the habit of rounding off my meal with a saucer of whipped cream, no sugar, and then cleansing my tongue with a special kind of spring water from a crevice in a sacred rock in the south of Italy. To ensure that the tests are not vitiated by any outside influences, it will be absolutely essential for the staff to observe these requirements. I usually take a little nap while digesting my dinner. I would request the staff to pre-heat an electric blanket to eighteen degrees Celsius and have some Schubert piano sonatas playing at low volume in the background; from his Romantic cycle, please. My qualifications as the ideal taster for a pet-food firm are obvious: I don't smoke, I am a teetotaller, I enjoy excellent health, I weigh not a gram more than is right for my time of life, I have the most elegant of table manners, and my tongue is a culinary seismograph far more refined than that of any top-flight restaurant critic. For reasons you will all understand, I cannot give my address here. I would therefore ask all interested captains of industry to send their applications, which should contain attractive financial terms, direct to the publishers. Kindly mark your envelopes: Francis, re self-sacrifice of.

CHAPTER 6

A
Soft
Touch

The cat's sense of touch and physical contact

For a long time the sense of touch, the fifth and last of the 'conventional' channels of perception, was rather looked down upon by scientists as lower than the other senses, probably because tactile sensations do not call on an independent and complex sensory organ such as an eye or an ear. In fact the entire surface of the skin is one large, extended sensory organ containing millions upon millions of microscopic touch receptors. Today we know that this diffuse organ of perception is very finely adjusted and makes an important contribution to our idea of ourselves. Even the bending of a single hair on the back of the hand can give rise to a distinct sensation. An adjustable electronic tappet making a tiny dent 0.01 millimetres deep on the skin surface will cause an unmistakable sense of pressure. However, the best example is probably provided by Braille, which consists of tiny raised dots. Blind people can pass their fingertips over these raised hieroglyphics at great speed, taking in every nuance of meaning in the classics of literature and science.

The sense of touch is also the most ancient and archaic of all the senses, and has made a profound mark on our idea of the world outside us. Charles Darwin pointed out that the first impressions of mammals are tactile in nature, since the foetus in its mother's uterus can feel a number of tactile sensations and mechanical stimuli. The baby uses its hands and mouth to investigate everything that interests it and thus gets an elementary impression of what those items are like. Many of the words we use to describe mental states refer to the sensation of touch. We *grasp* certain things, we are deeply *touched* by the way they *feel*, we *seize* an opportunity. If we find people *repellent* or even just *superficial*, we may stop getting *in touch* or *in contact* with them. As the famous ethologist Konrad Lorenz once cogently put it: 'To think is to move around in the area of the imagination.'

The sense of touch anchors living creatures to reality more than any other. Without tactile sensations we really would be 'ghosts in a material world', as the title of a song puts it. We are not totally persuaded that the world before our eyes is real until the moment when it becomes material and has substance. What we perceive with our other senses is merely a likely hypothesis which still requires tactile confirmation. Many important features of the environment are conveyed to us chiefly through touch; we need only think of properties such as softness, hardness, fluidity, elasticity, smoothness, roughness, etc. When we feel objects outside us, however, we are feeling ourselves at the same time. Can I say I am feeling a pencil, or should I say I feel my finger holding the pencil? We touch the world and thus bring it into contact with what matters most to us, ourselves.

What a person calls 'himself' or 'herself' actually consists to a great degree of a quantity of tactile impressions and memories. However, touch covers not just surface sensations but what is known as depth sensitivity. The joints, muscles and sinews also have touch receptors, registering tension, movement and strength. These 'proprio-sensors' give us a feeling of the position in which our extremities happen to be, even in the dark. This sense of position is active day and night; the very moment we wake up, an impression of just where our limbs are lying is fully present. Only when a part of the body has 'gone to sleep' because a nerve is numbed do we notice how unpleasant it is to lose the ability to feel ourselves. All our tactile impressions put together make us aware of the spatial extent of our bodies. This body pattern is in some ways the very heart of our sense of identity. People who have lost a part of the body in an accident or operation may still be suffering phantom pain years later. The affected person's body pattern has not yet dealt successfully with the loss of the limb and conjures up painful visions from memory.

Such philosophical reflections are very relevant to the present subject, because the world of the cat's tactile perception probably differs only very slightly from ours, as John Bradshaw points out. As in man, the naked ape, the surface of the cat's body has three main groups of sensors. The most important group, the mechano-receptors, responds to mechanical stimuli such as pressure and touch. Thermo-receptors register high or low temperatures, and nociceptors react to harmful stimuli and engender a subjective sense of pain. However, we still do not know for sure whether nociceptors really constitute a special, separate class of sensors all over the body. It could be that all the mechano-receptors and thermo-receptors send out pain signals themselves if they are over-stimulated. The pain when you knock your knee against the edge of a table may arise only from abnormal arousal of the tactile feelings. Heat may be painful only because 'normal' temperature sensors are over-stressed.

The cat's hairs – two hundred per square millimetre on the stomach, half that number on the back – grow in small tufts from fine sacs in the skin, the follicles. The root of every hair is in touch with several sensory nerve cells. But the bare skin between the hairs is in contact with nerves as well. The touch receptors are concentrated at these 'clearings' into small raised touch points, between seven and twenty-five of them per square centimetre. They are equipped with several different varieties of mechano-receptors which can distinguish between a wide spectrum of tactile stimuli, from touching to pushing, stroking, tickling, combing and brushing.

In the cat, as in ourselves, different parts of the body have different sensor densities. Humans have their greatest tactile ability at their fingertips, which can feel even extremely fine structures, for instance the points of Braille. On the upper arm, however, the sense of touch is rather poor, and most people cannot even feel if they are being touched by one or both points of a pair of scissors in that area. The cat's nose and the balls of its feet are its most sensitive tactile areas. The mechano-receptors on its front paws have an incredibly high sensitivity to impressions of movement and vibration, making the cat almost able to 'hear' with its paws. However, these sensors become useless as soon as the object being touched ceases to move. When the cat wants to feel immobile structures, it must pass its paws over them. Cats can often be seen systematically investigating some interesting new item. They usually extend a paw and touch the object or rub it, first gently and then more vigorously. The next step is to bring the nose into play. The extreme sensitivity of the paws is probably the main reason why cats loathe being struck in that area. In addition the claws, which can be shot out and retracted like flick-knives, have sensors at the base. It could be said, with some justification, that the cat's paws are independent sense organs.

Unfortunately, the cat shares its hypersensitivity to movement and vibration with other living creatures which mean it no good. The pupae of the cat flea make cunning use of vibrations at floor level. They lie motionless, hidden in the carpet, until a slight trembling tells them that their intended host the cat is coming. Then they jump on the unsuspecting victim. The last phase of their jump is guided by the cat's body warmth and the carbon dioxide in its breath. The pupa can wait for months or even years to be suddenly woken from its slumbers by the right 'vibes', like the Sleeping Beauty. Many a cat walking into a house that has stood empty for a long period has had an unpleasant surprise.

Almost all parts of the cat are equipped with mechano-receptors which are constantly telling the brain what forces are operating on the organ concerned. A very important member of the mechano-receptor family known as the Pacinian corpuscle shows considerable similarities with the stress indicators used in industry. The Pacinian corpuscles, onion-shaped and about a millimetre in size – positively gigantic as such gauges go – are structures filled with cellular liquid which pass on information about the slightest change of pressure on the nerve. They are found wherever the measurement of stress is biologically useful: in the skin, the ligaments of the intestines, the diaphragm and other flat structures subject to stress and to stretching. Cats can tell how full their digestive tracts are with the aid of Pacinian corpuscles. They work like the sensors measuring how full the petrol tank of a car is. Big cats, particularly lions and tigers, can devour huge quantities of meat. In the process, they sometimes reach the limits of what they can take, and in such cases Pacinian corpuscles probably act as an emergency brake preventing mechanical overstrain – in short, the lion might burst without them. Nature always has the best ideas, and pressure receptors in technology – for instance, in a pressure tank – are constructed on the model of Pacinian corpuscles.

All tactile information from the surface of the body is gathered in by the cerebral cortex, the furrowed and wrinkled appearance of which makes it resemble a walnut. Tactile data are processed by a department of their own, the 'somato-sensory cortex'. The entire surface of the body is topographically depicted in this 'tactile field', as if on a map. Consequently those parts of the body which are situated close together have the same neighbourly relationship in the cortex. The end result is to produce the image of a small man or woman in the brain. However, this image of the homunculus, as it is called, in the brain does not have the same proportions as its physical original, because the sensors are distributed over the surface of the body at different densities. The human homunculus appears as a curiously distorted monstrosity, with greatly swollen lips and fingertips. The counterpart to the homunculus in cats may be called the 'felinculus', and its picture appears in various books about Felidae, with the paws and the whole head, particularly the nose and tongue, shown in outsize dimensions.

The cat's stiff and extremely sensitive whiskers have unusually good computing abilities. They are anatomically described as vibrissae. These hypersensitive sensory hairs, which resemble a little forest of antennae on the cat's forehead, have a function similar to radar. Vibrissae are hairs which have undergone considerable further development, are rooted three times deeper than other hairs in the body tissue, and have unusually dense nerve contacts at the roots. On average cats have twenty-four whiskers above their top lips, twelve on each side, situated in four horizontal rows. The cat has similar vibrissae on other parts of its body, for instance on the cheeks, above the eyes, on the chin and at the back of the front legs, but what we usually think of as the whiskers are the really active ones.

Their most elementary function is to be a ruler or tape-measure; the cat can employ them to work out whether it can get through certain passages or small holes. Using its whiskers, it can make its way through a wheat-field without making the blades move and give its presence away, while at the same time its eyes are preserved from injury. The

whiskers and eyelids are linked by a reflex: the smallest touch, such as a blade of grass springing back, will immediately set off a protective blinking.

The vibrissae are very mobile and can be spread forward when the cat is feeling some object or pouncing on a mouse. They enable it to 'read' the structure of interesting items too close for the eye to focus on. The principle is the same as in blind people reading Braille with their fingertips. Most cats twitch their whiskers violently during what is called REM-sleep, when dreams and rapid eye movement occur. The ancient Chinese believed that cats were dreaming of mice, and nothing better has been suggested even in the most modern books on brain research. However, perhaps our sophisticated big-city cats do not dream of mice any more, but of a Promised Land full of fresh liver and open tins.

Many other animals which prowl through foliage and garbage in search of food by night have several whiskers pointing downwards from their chins. Taylor says that the tiny desert mouse, which can achieve very high speeds, uses two long vibrissae as a direction-finding system while it runs. The nimble rodent thus discovers the whereabouts of stones, holes and other obstacles in its path early enough to change direction. The cat's whiskers, says Fox, must also help it to locate the spatial origin of any suspicious scent. It can use them to snap up those small air currents which tell it both figuratively and literally which way the wind is blowing.

The cat can also get its bearings from these slight currents of air if it has to find its way in total darkness. Hunting at night as it does, it needs to be able to pass a number of objects both large and small in the dark without bumping into them. As it approaches, the barriers they set up cause tiny deviations of the normal circulation of the air. Thanks to the amazing sensitivity of its whiskers the cat literally 'gets wind' of these changes very early and can make its way elegantly past them. In a maze test Professor Leyhausen observed cats whose whiskers had been trimmed missing their way in the dark and wandering around hopelessly lost. These feline antennae are also essential for catching prey. With its vibrissae intact, the cat will successfully carry out the killing neck-bite peculiar to Felidae even in complete darkness. However, if its radar equipment is impaired it can kill mice only in the light. The system is obviously employed for long-distance location manoeuvres, discerning the outline of the prey's body in conditions where vision is poor, and guiding the cat's jaws towards its neck. It seems that the tips of the whiskers can scan the victim's outline in detail and inform the brain of the next step to be taken.

Cats blind from birth can find their way around remarkably well even without vision. They navigate an obstacle course with the unerring certainty of a sleepwalker, and an unsuspecting observer would never guess their handicap. This is partly because their hearing has improved to compensate, and has taken over a disproportionate number of nerve cells. Consequently, such animals can perceive a clearer 'auditory picture'. The sensitivity of a blind cat's whiskers also increases to gather an unusually large amount of information about the outside world.

This has recently been proved by J. P. Rauschecker, a cyberneticist at Tübingen. He noticed that blind cats had much longer, thicker whiskers than their sighted counterparts, and made particularly busy use of them. Their experiences are probably parallel to those of blind people who often have an impression that they can feel shadows or pressure falling on their faces, a phenomenon described medically as facial vision. Rauschecker suspects that the nerve centres in the brain which process signals from the whiskers are extended in blind cats and occupy areas intended for optical impressions. Cats, incidentally, may go blind if their food contains none of the amino acid taurine, which occurs only in meat (and tinned cat-food). Among other things, taurine deficiency severely damages the retina.

Many mother cats seem to feel that their offspring's long whiskers are a nuisance, and will actually nibble them off. However, this may be an educational expedient intended to prevent enterprising kittens from venturing too far from the nest too soon. Cats in general hate human beings to do anything to their sensitive and decorative whiskers. If the vibrissae are touched, they temporarily lose their sensitive powers of perception, which means that for the time being the cat is deprived of an important part of its vital information-gathering equipment. It is like shining a bright light into a human's eyes. Some cats do seem to like having their whiskers affectionately caressed, and will purr with contentment, but there can be few things worse for a cat than to have ignorant or naughty children cutting its whiskers off.

In spite of its high sensitivity to tactile stimuli, the cat's skin is surprisingly immune to variations of temperature. This is odd, for cats are always keen to make themselves as comfortable as possible in some warm, cosy spot. However, cats remain perfectly cool with skin temperatures of up to fifty-two degrees Celsius, while many humans find a mere forty-four degrees hard to tolerate. Cats will frequently singe their tails or fur by sitting on a hot stove and never notice. The mishap is not usually detected until the cat's owner smells the penetrating odour of burnt fur, and disparaging remarks about the pet's lack of intelligence may well be made. In fact the cause of this self-destructive behaviour is not stupidity but a blind spot in the sensory apparatus. It is surprising that cats, with their highly developed sense of smell, will ignore the acrid smell of their own singed rear ends; perhaps we can explain it by remembering that in its original ecological niche the cat was not yet prepared for the epoch-making discovery of fire. However, cats are also rather insensitive to extreme cold. They certainly prefer to be warm and comfortable, but they will quite happily walk over ice, and will sometimes drop off to sleep in the snow without getting chilblains. All organisms which can perceive injurious stimuli in the form of pain also have means of silencing this watch-dog of physical health. For instance, both humans and cats produce endorphins, the body's own anaesthetics, which have an opiate effect. Bruce Fogle suggests that cats manufacture particularly powerful endorphins. Even if they suffer severe injuries or broken bones, they will go away quietly and without making a fuss to some safe place where they can suffer in private. One result of this powerful pain-killing system is that vets often do not see sick cats until they are at a very advanced stage of illness, not because the cats have callous owners but because they are stoical creatures who prefer to keep their pain to themselves, like the North American Indians of old.

However, the nose and its immediate surroundings are an

exception. The area of the nose and upper lip is extremely sensitive to temperature and can perceive a change of one degree either way. Rockets carried on fighter planes often have heat-seeking radar helping them to find the way to their targets; kittens also have heat-seeking devices on their noses to help them find their way to the warmth of the maternal nest.

The touching way in which small kittens cuddle up to their mother is a clear demonstration that body contact is a deep-seated biological need. Directly after birth the mother begins an intensive and lengthy process of licking her babies, tending them with her tongue. This is the newborn kitten's first sensory experience, and for a long time it was thought to be exclusively a matter of hygiene and cleanliness. But closer observations, says the American anthropologist Ashley Montagu in his pioneering work on touching, quickly showed that maternal licking is absolutely essential to life. The area the mother licks most is around the genitals and anus; the mouth and stomach come next. No other activity takes up so much of her time as licking. Kittens whose mother neglects her maternal duty for any reason very often die from a failure of the excretory organs. It is clear that the kidneys, bowels and urinary tract require this tactile stimulation to become fully functional. Orphaned kittens being hand-reared in sterile conditions must always have their genital areas wiped with a piece of cotton wool after feeding.

The fact that kittens can empty their bladders only if the mother sets off what is called the urogenital reflex with her tongue makes sense in terms of evolutionary survival. It prevents them from soiling the nest with urine while the mother is away; the smell might attract beasts of prey with designs on tender kitten flesh. Later, the growing kittens learn how to urinate for themselves by watching their mother. The American writer Paul Kunkel describes an extreme case which shows how adaptable and good at learning cats are: a little tom kitten who was reared with a litter of puppies and learned from their mother soon got into the habit of lifting a leg and urinating on the nearest tree.

In humans, says Montagu, urogenital stimulation is not necessary because the mother's labour goes on long enough to provide the foetus with sufficient pressure and massage. In fact if a newborn baby is reluctant to take its first breath, it is an age-old tradition to encourage it with a slap on the bottom. Premature babies gain control of their bowel and bladder muscles later than other children. Finally, the bond between mother and child expressed by skin contact is illustrated by the way the mother's uterus contracts when her newborn baby is placed beside her. In the past babies were not put next to their mothers to sleep for the first twenty-four hours after birth because it was believed that the uterus would not calm down, but would 'scratch about inside the mother like a big mouse'.

Pregnant cats frequently and ostentatiously lick their genitalia and the lower parts of their bodies. This auto-stimulation seems to be necessary for the pregnancy to come to a successful conclusion. Mother cats who omitted such tactile stimulation have been found to have underdeveloped milk glands during the nursing period.

Several European languages describe uncouth people with poor social skills as 'unlicked' cubs or 'unlicked' bears.

Originally, as Montagu says, this was a reference to the widespread belief that the young of many animals came into the world in so undeveloped a state that the mother had literally to lick them into shape. There is a grain of truth behind this idea, although only in a metaphorical sense. Early body contact from licking, stroking and other affectionate caresses can influence an animal's entire physical and mental development. Mammals which receive plenty of tactile stimulation early in life will develop a more efficient immune system later, and be able to resist the causes of illness. Physical contact probably has an effect on the growth of the thymus gland, which manufactures the body's defence cells. Plenty of stroking in infancy will make the adult animal heavier, give it a glossier coat, and mean that it feels less anxious in threatening situations. Dairy experts know that cows milked by hand give better, richer milk than cows milked by machine. It has even been observed that hedgehogs suffer if the fleas they harbour in large numbers are removed. It is perfectly possible that they actually need the odd form of skin stimulation provided by their symbiotic fleas to help their blood circulate properly.

Some decades ago several famous studies provided dramatic evidence that baby monkeys (and human babies) will not thrive and may even die of 'hospitalisation' if they are deprived of the warmth of physical contact in their first years of life. Females who survive this horrific scenario in infancy generally grow up to be unloving mothers whose own offspring suffer the same sad fate. From the scientific point of view, stroking and petting induces the organism with its vegetative nervous system to switch into parasympathetic overdrive. The heartbeat slows, the digestive juices and saliva begin to flow, and the digestive system of the stomach and bowel area itself begins working. Lack of skin contact, however, produces diametrically opposite reactions and long-term vegetative stress.

Many monkeys and apes (and cats) practise intensive mutual grooming and de-louse or de-flea each other. This grooming not only cleanses the body of parasites and impurities, but also acts as social cement holding relationships and groups together. Our hairy cousins groom themselves with particular vigour just after a fierce fight. In these circumstances grooming is employed as a policy of détente, pouring oil on troubled waters. Monkeys at the lower end of the pecking order will also sometimes 'borrow' a baby from another monkey and parade with it in front of the dominant male in the group. The reactions aroused by a baby will calm even an angry boss, and many fierce feuds end in a deliberate process of child-care. Cats who are bored or do not know how to work off their aggression will frequently lick themselves as a displacement activity which also serves to decrease built-up tension.

A kitten may depend upon its daily dose of licking and stroking for life itself; in an adult cat, however, Fox believes, petting is purely for pleasure. Most cats are extremely keen to be petted, stroked and caressed at certain times; petting is a kind of feline opium. If cats should ever take over as rulers of the world they would all surely keep a *Homo sapiens domesticus* about the house – to open their tins and to stroke them. To be strictly honest, however, it has to be said that the feline clan once mastered the tin-opening knack themselves, back in the

mists of time. The awe-inspiring sabre-toothed tiger, whose majestic appearance enriched the fauna of the world aeons ago, had two great downward-pointing tusks which reached a length of up to twenty centimetres. There has been much discussion of the function of these outsize teeth. One hypothesis, says Andrew Kitchener, is that the great cat used its tools to crack the mighty armour of the extinct giant armadillo or glyptodont. Then it sank its tusks into the creature's shell, much as you pierce the top of a tin of condensed milk with a tin-opener.

Being stroked turns a cat on and allows controlled regression, an enjoyable return to the pleasures of infancy. Many cats demand their petting at such length and with such enthusiasm that they can be a positive nuisance to their exhausted owners. Some will become ferocious wild beasts if tickled on the stomach, with their soft under-parts exposed; others love it. One cat may like to be petted very firmly, almost scratched; another wants only very gentle stroking. Many cats like to have a human hand pet their faces just beside the mouth, while others reserve this privilege for cats. Some like to have their tails stroked; with others, the tail is strictly out of bounds. We can never really understand exactly what oceanic sensations go through the mind of a cat being petted, but the French writer Jean-Louis Hue has made a poetic stab at imagining what it feels like . . . 'a firework display with its preliminaries, its bright flares, its intermezzi, its pauses for rest and its closing bouquet, all to be imagined as taking place in inner space, irradiating the cat's body, spraying sensation between the nerves and blood vessels like catherine wheels, sparkling fountains, jets, stars, standing or circling suns.'

Not only do cats like to be stroked but sometimes, as Ulrich Klever reminds us, they will stroke us back in a loving and affectionate manner. They pass their paws over our skin, push their damp noses at us gently but with obvious intensity of feeling. These wonderful moments are the high spots of the relationship between humans and cats. Some people say that women are particularly inclined to keep cats because they find the silky touch of their fur pleasant and even erotic. However, it is unlikely, says Roger Caras, that in the relatively short history of their domestication (or self-domestication) cats have developed a special instinct for dealing with human beings. Cats are always very watchful when there are humans around, and since the days of ancient Egypt they have been looking at us with their large, impressive eyes, but it is probably nothing to do with the number of our legs. Kittens are notoriously inclined to plunge into every imaginable relationship whole-heartedly and with friendly curiosity: they are ready to make friends with rabbits, birds, guinea pigs, even rats and mice. No doubt cats, with their eye to the main chance, would have settled down just as happily with chimpanzees or gorillas if the apes had provided better service than mankind. Mark Twain once described the strange behaviour of a cat he saw in Marseille zoo: every day without fail it climbed up on an elephant's back to take a nap there in comfort. The elephant always objected to being made use of in this way and would sweep the mountaineer off with its trunk, but the cat was not about to give up, and kept trying to climb on again. Did it like the huge and gentle elephant, or

was it simply motivated by an opportunistic wish for a warm place to sleep?

A French poet once described sexual intercourse as the harmony of two souls and the contact of two epidermises, and indeed in humans the skin is not so much involved in any other pleasurable activity as in the tender foreplay of the sexual act. Sexual partners can give themselves countless pleasures through stimulation of the erogenous zones. Cats have a reputation for lechery because of their extended sexual orgies, but their erotic practices are not noted for the subtle artistry of the Kama Sutra. The chosen tom who allows himself to be seduced by the flattering yowls of a queen on call will generally initiate the first act in the drama of love by licking the back of his partner's ears. This caress is not usually regarded as having any sexual significance; it is thought that the prudent lover is simply pacifying his agitated mistress, who might well do him actual bodily harm in her heated condition. For the same reason, the male frequently bites the back of his sexual partner's neck while he is getting down to business. This is not a macho gesture designed to make the weaker sex submit, but an act of pure self-defence: it sets off the automatic reflex of 'freezing' while being carried, which goes back to kittenhood. When the mother cat applies this carrying grip to her kittens they are suddenly immobilised, and can then be carried away without any fuss in an emergency. The tom cat putting the bite on his partner in this way has a better chance of turning her back into a gentle kitten.

However, there may be more to it than that. A great many humans seem to enjoy giving or receiving 'love-bites'. The bite a man may inflict on his partner is usually part of foreplay, and given just before actual coitus. Sexual researchers believe that enjoyment of biting is to do with the wish to give a kiss more intense than ordinary kisses, a desire to leave a long-lasting mark and heighten tactile stimulation to its maximum.

The tom cat involuntarily does just that, in a different way. During the release of semen – and sexual intercourse takes the form of a 'quickie' in cats, penetration lasting at most ten seconds – the female cat gives an explosive scream and suddenly turns furiously on her mate. Arabian natural scientists of the early Middle Ages concluded that the tom was passing a painful ejaculate on to his lover. 'She is in great pain, because the sperm burns her, and she will scream until she has rid herself of it.' This mistake is also responsible for the horror story that tom cats were notorious infanticides: they were supposed to murder their own kittens and eat them with cannibalistic glee merely to persuade an unwilling partner to engage in another act of love, her wish for children being stronger than her fear of painful intercourse.

Today, there is another explanation for her change of mood: the penis of an entire tom has many little barbs at its tip which presumably cause pain inside the vagina. However, the biologist Andrew Kitchener does not agree with this widely held interpretation, and thinks it unlikely that the queen's sudden change of mood after penetration is dictated by pain. He believes it more probable that her defensive attitude is a protective measure intended to prevent the tom, a stranger to her, from confusing his sexual partner with his next meal. Leyhausen had in fact already established that queens who have been associated with one particular gentleman for some time almost never indulge in post-coital attacks. Moreover, the female partners in this fertility ritual very soon recover their composure and prepare for the next amorous session with obvious enthusiasm. It is hard to imagine, says Kitchener, that female cats would do 'it' so often if it really hurt them.

In any case, the tom cat's penis is not constructed as it is with a view to sado-masochistic pleasure, but as a practical biological strategy. The violent stimulation of the vagina (perhaps in conjunction with the love-bite) sets off a chain of hormonal reactions which culminate in ovulation, the process whereby an egg capable of fertilisation is shed by the ovary and enters the Fallopian tube, like a cartridge being shifted from the magazine into its firing position. Induced ovulation is another sign that the cat is still a solitary hunter at the bottom of its heart. Ovulation of this kind is characteristic of creatures which, like cats and camels, are loners and so cannot be sure of having a male partner available for them at regular periods of fertility. Induced ovulation ensures that every encounter in the heat of passion can be fertile.

In humans such induction of ovulation is not necessary, since a woman ovulates spontaneously in a monthly rhythm. However, the American sociobiologist Margie Profet argues that many other living creatures can also shed eggs spontaneously as a result of external stimulation. Perhaps methods of oral stimulation in human sexual intercourse are an atavistic return to our mammalian past.

In any case, it is not certain that induced ovulation is a characteristic of all cat species. It is easy to imagine spontaneous ovulation in the lioness, who lives and makes love in a community or pride of lions. For some reason or another, the female lynx is also thought to ovulate without external stimulation. The ovulation of the domestic cat can be artificially induced if the vagina is carefully stimulated with a soft, blunt instrument. Veterinary surgeons and experienced breeders sometimes do this to end a call that has gone on too long. Some insatiable queens (particularly Siamese) suffer from non-stop calling, corresponding to what would be called nymphomania in humans.

The tom cat's penis has another peculiarity besides its barbs. As with many other beasts of prey it is reinforced with a bone, the baculum. In the venerable fraternity of the Felidae, however, the baculum is considerably smaller than in the dog family, for instance. We may suppose that the instrument of desire can overcome gravity in cats without any bony prosthesis, purely by the erectile power of passion and the circulation of the blood. Remarkably, in Felidae the female of the species also has the beginnings of a kind of baculum, inside the clitoris. According to one theory, this hard foreign body may even be responsible for the shriek she utters during the brief act of love; perhaps the thing presses and hurts like a pebble in one's shoe.

Although the physical conditions are present it is an open question whether female cats have an orgasm or not. To be honest, scientists simply do not know when and why nature handed her children this bonus of sexual climax. In principle it is perfectly possible to reproduce without sexual pleasure – just as various churchmen would wish. The American zoologist John Alcock said he kept watching carpenter bees copulating but could not make out whether they felt anything in the least like our ideas of pleasure. The simpler living creatures are, the more difficult it is to read ecstasy and sexual pleasure into their reactions. The problems are even greater than for a human Casanova who has to take a woman's word for it.

In any case, most mammals display a striking interest in sex and are ready to go to considerable trouble to get it. This is the best indication that they enjoy it. The whole behaviour of the male rat suggests that he is having a wonderful orgasm during coitus. After ejaculation he thrusts hard once more, slowly gets up on his hind legs, and gets a glassy look in his eyes which leaves little to the imagination. Most scientists think that male mammals at least, the tom cat included, reach a peak of sexual pleasure. In terms of evolutionary development, after all, it makes sense for male animals to feel an urgent desire for orgasm, since they can increase their genetic fitness and beget more viable offspring if they randily seize every sexual opportunity on offer. On the other hand it would be unwise for females, who have to carry the main burden of reproduction, to embark on any and every brief encounter.

The contribution made by the male to reproduction is therefore inextricably linked with orgasm. The female, however, can be fertilised without orgasm and even without any pleasant sensations. However, there are also clear signs that the female orgasm fulfils important and independent biological functions. During climax there is a measurable pressure in the uterus which can help to suck up sperm. This could give the female some control over which male is allowed to leave his genetic fingerprints.

If female cats have a strong physical urge to have inter-course several times running, it is because there are consider-able advantages attached. Sometimes their sexual partner is exhausted after the first few encounters, while the female herself is only just getting into her stride. This motivates her to seduce a successor, or several successors, to bring the curve of tension to its crowning conclusion. The same strategy also blurs paternal responsibility: all cats who took part in the orgy must reckon with the possibility that the resulting kittens are their own. Males who are not sure of their paternity will treat the lady of their heart kindly for reasons of genetic selfishness alone, and will not attack her offspring, who might after all be their own flesh and blood. Perhaps this is why infanticide by the father is much less common in cats than various horror stories would have us believe.

After the sexual act the queen puts on a lascivious post-coital performance, rolling about on the ground, purring and rubbing herself against all kinds of objects. Alfred Kinsey, the pioneer of research into human sexuality, thinks such behaviour a clear indication of the after-tremors of a mighty orgasm. He also measured such biosignals as pulse and breathing in cats who had just been copulating. From his account of it, values in female as well as male cats shot up so high that they could be explained only by a volcanic eruption of sexual energy.

Finally, we can see how much cats enjoy sex from the fact that they sometimes indulge in it in one or other of the forms not authorised by the Vatican, which preaches that the call of nature should be answered only for purposes of propagation, and preferably with feelings of regret. The subject of masturbation, perversion and other extras is often left out of books on animal behaviour, even the more liberal sort, or reduced to bizarre exceptions connected with abnormal living conditions. A work on the physiology of love published in 1918 devotes two hundred and eighty-three pages to the various kinds of carnal lust in fauna, but dismisses masturbation briefly with the terse remark that 'there is nothing unnatural in nature'.

Even the great writer Mark Twain was not immune to mistaken judgements on the subject, believing that the monkey was the only animal but man to practise that art, and that was what made him our brother. Today biologists know better: all higher forms of life are our brothers (and sisters). Sex in the first person singular has been recorded in kangaroos, whales, giraffes, doves and budgerigars, dogs and cats, to name but a few. The breadth of range suggests that the higher animals as a whole pay attention to their own genitals from time to time. This autoeroticism – a word which has nothing to do with the modern male's passion for his wheels – is by no means a neurosis induced by confinement. All forms of behaviour observed in captivity, in zoos and among domesticated species also occur in the wild; for instance, there are bull elephants who affectionately pleasure their own penises with their trunks, there are female chimpanzees who will introduce sticks bitten to suitable size into their vaginas, and there are dolphins who blissfully rub their erogenous zones against the US Navy torpedoes they borrow.

If other creatures reach the peaks of pleasure on their own, the Felidae cannot be lagging behind. Paul Leyhausen records that a tom cat overcome by his libido will frequently lick his partially or entirely erect penis. It is hard to say whether this solitary form of fellatio is intended to get the precious instrument into working order or whether the voluptuary is giving himself a foretaste of the joys to come. At the beginning of adolescence and just after castration, cats in a state of excitement will mount the arm of a human, a cushion, or a piece of furniture, and give themselves relief with rubbing movements. The cat psychiatrist Peter Neville once even had to treat a purring patient whose obscure object of desire was a very strange one indeed: a particular knob on the radiator. Whether the patient actually felt anything like passion and was able to see the point of his therapy must remain an open question.

The intoxicating aromas emanating from a queen on call can get tom cats so randy that they will attack harmless items like teddy bears and other stuffed toys and try to copulate with them in the unmistakable manner of Fritz the Cat. In experiments made to study this phenomenon the would-be Casanovas sometimes leapt up as if electrified, and snatched their love surrogates from the researcher with the typical neck-bite of intercourse before it could be put down on the ground. If the data so far collected are reliable, female animals pleasure themselves more rarely than males, but such statements should be approached with caution. Male erection and ejaculation is easier to classify as masturbation than the quiet bliss enjoyed by Ms Felix as she rubs herself on the ground.

According to Darwinist dogma, only modes of behaviour which can bring the individual reproductive advantage will

survive in the evolutionary process. So one naturally wonders (like the Pope) how the squandering of valuable semen can be any use to the production of new life. In fact British biologists recently showed that sex at first hand does have reproductive value. The sperm of masturbating males is fresher and more vigorous next time they perform the 'real' sexual act. Younger sperm are more successful if sperm of several aspirants to paternity are competing in the body of a female. The masturbator is giving his sperm a good start in the great swimming race for the egg cell. Females also give themselves better chances of reproduction by masturbating: they are keeping the muscles of their vagina fit and their vaginal secretions fresh. So autoeroticism does in fact in-directly serve the reproductive purpose and could even earn the blessing of the Vatican as a flanking manoeuvre.

As late as 1972 a well-respected researcher into sexuality was teaching that homosexuality occurred only in human beings and nowhere else in the animal kingdom. He was wrong. For some time it was one of the best-kept secrets of behavioural science that forms of homosexual love have spread right through the family tree of living creatures. A German ethologist who studied the homosexual activities of guinea pigs thought the phenomenon did occur in many species of birds and mammals, but was usually kept out of the data and swept under the carpet of science. All aspects of homosexual behaviour possible in human beings are also found in closely approximating versions in animals. In cats too, both sexes are capable of switching roles, at least sometimes. According to Leyhausen, the act is a perfect copy of 'normal' copulation up to the moment of penetration. Not

only the female domestic cat but some of her wild relations have been observed engaging in lesbian affairs.

The assumption that it is impossible for tom cats to take on the female role has now been refuted. Male cats can indeed assume the female position on occasion. They just have to be feeling in the mood – and not in a rape situation. But even that can occur, mirroring various American police or penitentiary films. Strange tom cats put in a cage with its established owner will frequently become his sexual victim.

But it is very rare for cats to cross the sexual barriers separating them from other species, although Neville does tell the story of the ginger cat Thumper, brought to him for treatment because of his inclination to sodomy. Thumper was obsessed with the charming female dachshund who shared his home, and kept trying to seal his love with physical union. The explanation for this uncontrollable desire turned out to be purely medicinal. The dachshund bitch was suffering from a tumour in her glandular tissue, and kept spraying large quantities of that feline pheromone which turns cuddly pets into ravening sexual brutes.

Comments by Francis

Love – I hear words like thermo-receptors, follicles, even non-stop calling, but do I hear the word love? No. Typical of the naked ape: even when discussing the most romantic of the cat's senses, they bring out their tape-rules and microscopes and make desperate efforts to reduce passion to a mathematical formula. Our skin and fur are an ocean of tenderness, and human hands should be like sensitive ships sailing over its waves of pleasure. But that's

Homo sapiens *for you: always wanting to reduce himself and his fellow creations to machines, regarding emotions as the inevitable exhaust gases. However, if everything's going to be made so automatic there's a danger that humans may not be needed any more. I'm planning to act on that notion in future. So let me first suggest the construction of a mechanical petting and stroking device for cats. What would it look like? Well, first it ought to have nice soft upholstery upon which the object of the exercise could lie comfortably, all four limbs outstretched, with a large opening just beneath the stomach. There'd be a stick with peacock feathers, rather like a percussion brush as used by jazz musicians, swinging rhythmically up and down underneath my device, every movement tickling the subject's belly in a provocative manner. Two hydraulic arms would descend from above. They would have adjustable pads on their ends to stroke and massage the cat's back, and they might close in together on reaching the rear end to form a ring of medium firmness through which the tail could be raised aloft. Rubber fittings like fingers would scratch the subject behind the ears, an elastic brush would keep combing his fur, blunted iron claws would scratch any areas of skin that happened to be itching, and the entire mechanism would rock to and fro and up and down like a turbo-driven cradle, making the whole experience a tactile orgy. I must say there's something very seductive about this vision, and I have to put the brake on my powers of imagination if I'm not to go right off the idea of that makeshift expedient called man. You may object, of course, that no cat would consent to get into such a miracle machine, that it would be soulless, cold and, yes, well, loveless. But didn't they say the same when inflatable rubber dolls were invented? I tell you, just try putting a device like that on the market – and then we'll see!*

Sense, Super-sense or Nonsense?

Unusual perceptive abilities of the cat

A ll cultures familiar with cats have credited them with access to the supernatural and a mysterious world beyond our own. However, these notions of a mystery which is beyond everyday reality and cannot be perceived by the conventional senses are inextricably intertwined with the religious and philosophical beliefs of whatever period is concerned. The Egyptians thought that the cat could see the kingdom of the sun, invisible to human eyes; the Middle Ages saw reflections of hell-fire in the cat's eyes; and in today's enlightened high-tech society the animal's 'paranormal' abilities are dissected in the clinical jargon of science. Parapsychology employs rhetoric drawn from the field of psychoanalysis to explain the allegedly 'clairvoyant' gifts of our domestic pets. The theory it proposes is that the invisible ether around us is constantly filled with vibrations, the breeding ground of psi phenomena and extrasensory perception. In 'normal' people who lack the abilities of a psychic medium, a kind of mental censorship is alleged to come into play, blocking reception of this occult channel. The theory takes this to be a constraint similar to that exercised by the superego which blanks out our illicit desires. Animals, however, and more particularly animals like cats, are allegedly free of such mental censorship and can thus listen in on extrasensory frequencies. The legendary bracketing of cats with women seems to rear its head again here. Since time immemorial, women have been thought to possess the greatest abilities as mediums, and a talent for soothsaying and clairvoyance. Second sight is a female attribute.

Some of the 'extra-ordinary' sensory abilities of the cat are to be found in the region of established fact and obey laws familiar to us from human physiology. As anyone knows who has ever seen next door's cat strolling along the garden fence with the dreamy grace of a ballet dancer, cats have an excellent sense of balance. For a hunter who usually has to get food while jumping and climbing, survival is always a tightrope act. Cats can keep their balance so well because their bodies react with extreme speed and sensitivity to every change of position. On superficial observation, the sense of balance does not seem to work like a real 'sense' registering information about the outside world. It is more reminiscent of motor skills like those of a ballerina or an acrobat, who can perform amazing tricks with their bodies. But in all such dazzling acrobatics, the brain must be kept constantly informed about the position of the body in relation to the earth's field of gravity. The sense of balance provides data on every deviation from the norm so that the body can counter it effectively.

Even when we are sitting with our eyes closed inside a jet plane flying at high speed, we never have the least doubt of the location of 'up' and 'down'. We can also say at any time whether the aircraft is climbing or losing height, or whether its speed has changed. The organ of balance, or vestibular system, is a kind of measuring instrument providing information about situation and speed. It is located in the inner ear and functions (to simplify matters considerably) on the principle of a spirit level. It consists of several chambers filled with fluid, at right angles to each other, lined with tiny, sensitive hairs. When the body changes position the fluid is set in motion and stimulates the sensory hairs, which immediately send their message to the brain.

Data from the inner ear are processed by a specialized auxiliary computer, the cerebellum. The cerebellum is like a miniature edition of its big brother, the main brain, and lies beneath the rear section of the cerebral cortex. The job of this coordination centre is the automatic correction of errors. It recognises what the position of the body ought to be, keeps watch for deviations from that norm, and intervenes at once if the actual position of the body is wrong. The cat's brain, in other respects very like the human brain, is distinguished by having a very much larger cerebellum. Consequently its sense of balance has a particularly large calculating capacity at its disposal. This fact explains its ability to move with elegant precision among your precious china ornaments. Its famous gift for landing on all fours also derives from its outsize navigational organ. Information about the fall causes the cat to turn its head as it rushes down, so that it is held horizontal, in the correct position. A reflex then brings the rest of the body into line with the head.

We probably have so little awareness of the way our sense of balance works because the activity of the cerebellum is usually automatic and subconscious. Sometimes, however, we can actually sense its functioning, for instance when climbing the steps of an escalator which is not moving. We suddenly get a vague, dizzy feeling similar to sea sickness or travel sickness. The cerebellum is probably already pre-programmed for the moving escalator by a kind of conditioning, and at the mere sight of the steps it takes those measures which would normally enable a passenger to keep his balance. However, as the steps are not in fact moving, this activity has nowhere to go – and produces the odd, rocking sensation. People who have suffered damage to the cerebellum have great difficulty with their balance and cannot even carry a cup of coffee to their lips without spilling some. They make the first large sweeping movement towards the mouth, but the small, corrective manoeuvres miss their intended mark.

Travel sickness is usually the result of excessive stimulation of an over-taxed sense of balance. Cats seem to be immune to it, probably because of their highly developed cerebellum, and so travelling by car seldom gives them any trouble. In past centuries many ship's cats did their duty catching rats on board merchant vessels without complaining. In terms of evolutionary biology, however, it is difficult to work out why many living creatures react to certain unusual movements with nausea and vomiting. As a rule evolutionary biologists consider what hidden advantages a given biological phenomenon may confer, or whether it made some kind of sense in the past which has been retained in stunted form.

In fact some animal species are particularly susceptible to feeling sick when moving, including horses, apes and monkeys and certain fish, while others, including cats and rabbits, have a natural immunity. But in what respect does a cat resemble a rabbit and not a chimpanzee? Many scientists believe that nausea felt only during movement has no useful purpose, but it does when it serves to remove poisons that have been swallowed from the body. Travel sickness would then be the coincidental side effect of the animal's reaction to movements of the head and eyes which occur in cases of food poisoning – and thus, unfortunately, during certain movements outside itself. Species fixated on a certain kind of diet in the wild, like the cat, do not need this protective mechanism because they are not about to experiment (as omnivores do) and are not in much danger of poisoning themselves. Confirmation of this theory is provided by the fact that even creatures prone to travel sickness do not suffer from it as infants. In the first phase of life, their ancestral nourishment is more than likely to be safe.

Surprising as it may sound, even the relaxed, equable cast of mind typical of most cats may have something to do with their powerful vestibular apparatus. There is a considerable grain of truth in the metaphorical term 'mental balance'. A well-balanced body is obviously likely to house a well-balanced mind; there is usually a healthy cerebellum behind a healthy cerebrum. American psychologists have observed that 'problem' children and young people usually have vestibular disturbances and cannot stand absolutely straight on one leg with their eyes closed. The connection between balance and sensation in the brain has been mapped out: there are direct, fast-moving nervous channels which lead from the cerebellum to the sensory centres and the pleasure centre below the skull. The sense of balance is active long before birth and enables the foetus to feel the rocking, rhythmic movements of its mother in its primal watery element. The system also requires suitable stimulation from an early stage; that stimulation is felt as pleasurable and encourages healthy development of the brain. This probably accounts for the primeval pleasure felt by babies (and kittens) being rocked gently in a cradle and playing games that make them dizzy. Children's hospitals in the USA have applied these findings to practical purposes and equipped their incubators with water beds. As a result, premature babies thrive better and suffer less from heart problems and breathing difficulties. Moreover, a vestibular 'firework display' may be the partial explanation for the strange magic of our dreams. In dreaming sleep, the organ of balance acts oddly, indulging in wild and chaotic discharging of its energy, feelings such as astronauts experience when weightless in space. Cats, incidentally, are cut out for space travel. At the end of the sixties NASA faced the problem of devising some means not involving mechanical drives whereby its astronauts could steer themselves during free movement in conditions of weightlessness. Cats were filmed in free fall, and gave the flight designers helpful hints about the way the space travellers should manoeuvre.

Not so very long ago, humans used the cat's large cerebellum for very down-to-earth pragmatic purposes. In 1961 the rice harvest on Borneo was threatened by a plague of mice. Without hesitation, the government had five hundred cats flown in from Singapore. Because of the urgency, this mobile operational unit was parachuted straight down into the affected areas. The mouse terminators set to work immediately after landing.

Bradshaw tells us that cats also have a relatively good sense of time. This is not a sense in the strict meaning of the word; after all, minutes and seconds are not physical events in the outside world which the brain might perceive with a special sensor. But cats can distinguish between two notes one of which is held for four seconds and the other for five seconds. They also quickly understand that they must delay a certain reaction (for instance, pressing a button) for a few seconds if the delay is necessary for success (a reward in the shape of food). The cat's chronological sense, says Fox, is something most cat-owners know from first-hand experience. Cats soon notice, for instance, that their human companions regularly get out of bed at a certain definite time – and they will take to creating uproar a minute or so before the alarm goes off, engendering considerable anti-cat feeling, particularly during holidays or at weekends.

But cats can also adjust to time schemes in which events recur at weekly intervals. An example is given by Gustav Eckstein, a professor of psychology at Cincinnati University. His cat Willi, who led a free-ranging life on campus, used to come to the kitchen door at 7.30 p.m. sharp every Monday, demanding to be fed, and then make off again in what looked like a purposeful manner. After a while this made Professor Eckstein so curious that one Monday he followed his four-footed friend right across the campus. The trail ended at the entrance to the gynaecological hospital, where the cat sat for two full hours staring as if spellbound through the window into a lighted room. The professor, not wishing to appear a Peeping Tom, did not venture to glance into the room himself until the third time he had followed the cat, when he finally discovered the reason for this strange conduct. At 7.45 precisely the women in the hospital's recreation room began their weekly Bingo game, which the cat watched to the end, fascinated.

Another example of the sense of weekly rhythm is provided by the well-known British zoologist Maurice Burton. He observed that a street trader used to appear with his barrow at a certain London crossroads every Tuesday afternoon, selling butchers' left-overs as pet-food. This kindly soul was in the habit of distributing scraps to four-legged onlookers when he cut up the portions of meat. For a period of years, therefore, all the neighbourhood cats would gather at the corner of the street just before twelve every Tuesday, waiting for the generous cat's-meat man. Not one of the semi-feral animals was to be seen there at the same time on other days of the week.

Finally, the Reverend Mr Wood, a nineteenth-century clergyman and naturalist, paid tribute to his grey cat Prettina's finely tuned sense of time. Wood was bedridden for a long time by chronic illness. Throughout this period, Prettina acted as nurse and morale-booster. Mr Wood wrote that it was wonderful to see how quickly she grasped the different times at which he had to take food or medicine, and if his human attendant fell asleep at night she would do her utmost to wake the man. The most extraordinary thing, he said, was that she never went wrong by as much as five minutes in estimating time, even at the dead of night. He wondered what means the little creature used to count the passing moments, at the same time paying attention to the attendant and his duties. Something other than reason, he thought, must have been involved.

A sense of the passing of time is of crucial importance for survival in the wild. Wild cats have to check very closely on when they can go out hunting and when they should leave the coast clear for physically superior competitors. In the wild, cats also have to synchronise their timetable with the rhythm of the lives of the creatures on which they prey. And after all, domestic cats depend on making the time schemes of their owners part of their own routine. A sense of time in the wild usually means that the organism has a biological clock which it can use to judge the amount of time passing. The bodies of mammals produce many constantly recurring oscillations, for instance the beating of the heart or the rhythmic discharges of certain nerve cells. However, we have no idea just *what* oscillating bio-signals the cat uses to measure time.

The dictatorship of the clock is a human invention. We need our chronometers because most of our activities are connected with the divisions of the clock-face. Work begins at a certain time of day; travel timetables, appointments, TV transmission times are all precisely fixed. Cats, on the other hand, can usually get their bearings from the rhythm of the

natural world, according to Caras. You do not need an alarm clock to tell you that you are hungry and had better go hunting. Winds come and go at particular places with calculable regularity. Plants have their own periodic cycles, some measured in hours, others in months. Daylight length is also bound to a recurrent chronological cycle. We probably have no real idea of the vast spectrum of signals and vibrations which the cat employs when locking into the oscillation of the universe.

It would therefore be very rash to suspect extrasensory capabilities such as precognition the moment cats seem to be visited by strange forebodings. It is frequently said that certain kinds of bizarre and nervous behaviour show cats have a 'sixth sense' for certain imminent events (for instance, a planned journey or the arrival of a baby). Cats watch us very closely, and the regular rhythm of our life-style gives them a sense of security. We do not have to speculate wildly to imagine that the slightest deviations from or changes in the routine will enable them to suspect that something is up, whereupon they will show their displeasure in every way they can.

The belief that cats have a phenomenal homing instinct is so deeply rooted that the mass media, at periodic intervals, solemnly celebrate it with new and wonderful examples. Almost every week you can read how a cat came home X months or years after it had been left somewhere miles away. In most cases a journey of less than fifty kilometres is involved, but accounts of cats undertaking tremendous odysseys are proliferating. For instance, the Americans like tales of cats successfully completing journeys of thousands of miles from coast to coast. The trip usually takes in various exotic scenes of American pop culture and is suspiciously reminiscent of that Hollywood genre known as the road movie. It is not surprising if tales of cats and dogs undertaking incredible journeys to make their way home are featured in animated films.

If we start to investigate these amazing stories methodically we must first distinguish between two basically different kinds of pilgrimage, suggests Michael W. Fox: the conventional sort, in which the cat finds its way to its old home from some other place, and the more extravagant variant, in which the animal follows an owner who has moved house to his new home, a long way away and entirely unknown to the cat. The second variant cannot be explained by even the most extreme and extra-ordinary sensory skills, and is thus called 'psi-trailing' and allotted to the realm of parapsychology.

Stories of cats returning to an existing home can be explained, at least in theory, by means of amazing but none the less realistic sensory skills. A frequently cited experiment also shows that there could be something in them. It was conducted at the Zoological Institute of Kiel University in Germany. The zoologists freed cats into large cages several miles from their homes. These cages had mazes inside them, with exits pointing in various different directions. Most cats promptly chose the exit pointing to home and ignored all other ways through the maze. However, the same thing did not occur when the distance from home was over twelve kilometres. There are various indications of ways in which the cats could have got their bearings. As mentioned above, Leyhausen suspects that a cat carries an aural map of its home

in its head, and works its way towards it by some direction-finding signal – for instance, a factory siren, a church clock, or the sound of a river running.

Another possibility, says Roger Caras, is that cats take their bearings from the position of the sun. If you free a cat several hundred kilometres from its usual home, you are also shifting the perceived angle of incidence of that heavenly body by a certain amount. The cat, noticing this irregularity, would really be instinctively trying to restore the right order of things – which would set it on the path leading home. Finally, we might also consider the earth's geo-magnetic field, the intensity of which varies distinctly from one place to another. It has been known for some time that certain animal species (for instance, whales) are equipped with compass-like sensors allowing them to navigate over great distances. It is perfectly possible that cats may have such a 'magnetic sense'.

However, these speculations all presuppose that the published stories are based on objective fact, and it seems that none of the reported incidents has been confirmed by strict, neutral, controlled scientific methods. They are all 'anecdotal' accounts from individual people. Consequently the entire varied spectrum of human motive – from enthusiasm through vanity to deception and delusion – may have played a part. This argument weighs particularly heavily when you stop to think that for every cat said to have found its way home, thousands of others remain lost – and no one makes a news story of that. Strictly speaking, indeed, it is impossible to test a cat's ability to find its way home scientifically. You would have to take a representative sample of cats to a distant spot and abandon them, which is out of the question if only for ethical reasons, since even the most credulous must suspect that a number of cats would get lost for good. In fact back in the nineteenth century George Romanes, a young friend of Charles Darwin, provided a foretaste of the kind of fiasco one might expect. The inquiring naturalist took a whole carriage-load of startled cats from their homes in the London suburbs and released them on Wimbledon Common. 'The result was chaos and a multitude of disorientated cats, with Romanes concluding that cats were "exceedingly stupid",' Bruce Fogle tells us.

A belief in the cat's amazing talent for navigation seems to have arisen only in the last few decades. In previous historical periods the cat was actually thought very bad at finding its way, unlike the dog. This is obvious, for instance, in E. T. A. Hoffmann's novel; at one point in the book his feline hero Murr unwittingly falls asleep in a horse-drawn cart and is suddenly and involuntarily driven several blocks away from home. Murr is wholly confused, and finds his way back only when guided by his friend the poodle Ponto. Master Abraham, believing that Murr has found his way home alone, is much surprised, and even quotes the scientific authorities of the day, who considered cats hopeless at navigation.

Such doubts are even more relevant to parapsychological psi-trailing. Some decades ago the famous American parapsychologist J. B. Rhine made a statistical analysis of all such cases reported to his laboratory. There were fifty-four in all: twenty-eight dogs, twenty-two cats and four birds. In the USA a story about a New York veterinarian made the headlines in a particularly big way. The veterinarian left his cat behind in the Big Apple when he moved to California.

Several months later an optically identical double of the cat loudly demanded to be let into the new home and made straight for his favourite armchair. The veterinarian, unable to believe his eyes, immediately felt for a particular identifying spot on the animal's tail. Sure enough, there was the mark by which he could recognise the cat: a kink in the tail-bone caused by an old bite. Some people probably have a strong need to believe that cats, with their nine lives, have magical or extrasensory gifts, and a more realistic explanation may seem dull and prosaic by comparison. For instance, it is realistic to point out that cats are good confidence tricksters. What is likely to happen when a tabby cat suddenly walks into a house and acts as if the place belongs to it? More people will fall in love with the idea that this is their own old Puss who went missing three years ago. As Plutarch pointed out, love blinds us to the beloved object.

There have also been parapsychological experiments with cats who were required to find the only way through a simple maze leading to food. Ventilators were switched on above the maze to obliterate any traces of scent. The chances of a cat's finding the way at once purely by accident were equal, but it turned out that some of the cats were right more often than the statistics would lead one to expect. Later, these results were criticised as not being quite beyond reproach: traces of scent had obviously not been entirely eliminated.

In the era of New Age enthusiasms it is increasingly usual for mysterious phenomena not immediately susceptible to logical explanation to be linked with supernatural and paranormal forces. Again, there is a desire for mystery and wonder behind such attitudes. Yet the scientific truth is often much more fascinating, illustrating as it does the breathtaking creativity and beauty of evolution. The cat, of all animals, has inexhaustible supplies of the natural magic with which evolution endowed its mysterious creations. Or as Lessing put it: 'The greatest of marvels is the fact that most true and genuine marvels can seem to us so ordinary.' So ordinary, indeed, that many people feel an urgent need to boost the feline marvel artificially with various kinds of metaphysical gobbledygook. And yet cats need psi abilities much less than human beings, since their excellent sensory organs leave the capabilities of any two-legged 'medium' far behind. As Desmond Morris rightly says, explaining mysterious phenomena by means of a psi factor is basically boring and unrewarding. The line taken by the psi theory is that the cat has magical powers, full stop, and so any search for the mysterious and interesting procedures behind the phenomena is nipped in the bud.

We do not need to call on any psi factor to understand why cats sometimes act strangely before a major earthquake and agitate to be let out of doors. On occasion cat-owners who complied with the odd demands of their feline companions may even have saved their own lives by doing so. Such incidents are now being investigated by serious academic institutes, and some day they could help with the introduction of a biological early warning system. The Chinese have already made use of such warnings in the great earthquake of 1975 in the Manchurian province of Liaoning, saving over ten thousand people from certain death, and in the Friuli region of Italy mother cats carried their kittens out of doors hours before the earthquake of 1976 began.

We may assume that cats, with the seismographically sensitive touch receptors on their paws, have felt certain vibrations preceding the major tremors. Or perhaps the change in the earth's magnetic field (or static electricity), which is registered before an earthquake, has irritated their hypersensitive nerves. During the Second World War, cats in London left the buildings which were about to be hit by bombs. The people of London were soon going down into their air raid shelters for safety if cats became restless when the alarm went, but not if they ignored the sirens. It is easy to imagine that, finely attuned to vibrations as they are, cats could pick up certain imperceptible vibrations of approaching aircraft. Perhaps they had simply connected this conditioned stimulus with its dreadful after-effects in the classic Pavlovian manner. In any case, the feline air raid warning squad was awarded the Dickin Medal before the end of the Second World War. Its inscription runs 'We also serve', a far from feline sentiment.

A four-year-old tabby called Dammit won her spurs as an air raid warden during the war; she warned the Americans on the Solomon Islands of the approach of Japanese aircraft. Not only that: she could tell 'one of our own' from the enemy planes. Her radar did not react to American aircraft.

Similar reactions are sometimes shown by cats just before a volcanic eruption, says Caras. Again, there are several possible explanations. Perhaps the animals feel slight seismic disturbances or an almost imperceptible change in soil temperature. Or perhaps the high sound of gases escaping from the earth's crust, something beyond the range of our own hearing, rings an alarm bell in the cat. It is remarkable that in the ruins of the Italian city of Pompeii, which was covered in lava when Vesuvius erupted in the year AD 79, scarcely any remains of cats have been preserved. The Roman writer Pliny the Elder, the man who had made such remarkably acute observations on cat behaviour, lost his life in the devastating rain of lava that fell on Pompeii. The most industrious naturalist of the Roman era, who left a natural history in more than thirty volumes, was too curious and ventured too close to the scene of destruction. There were self-styled cat experts in all the high cultures of antiquity, and their wise sayings about their mysterious pets not infrequently helped them to fame and fortune.

Many plaster casts of human beings taken by surprise in the natural catastrophe of the eruption may be seen in Pompeii today. The people of ancient Rome certainly kept cats, but there is nothing odd about the fact that those animals made off at the first sign of trouble. In the superstitious Middle Ages their 'prophetic' talent was their undoing, and they were burnt at the stake because they were believed to have forbidden knowledge.

Comments by Francis

Well, of course the last part of this chapter is total nonsense. We do have paranormal faculties like psi and ESP and whatever you want to call it, we do get instinctive advance warning of natural catastrophes, and we are far superior in every way to human beings in extrasensory matters. But making a time-consuming effort to persuade them otherwise at this point would be something I would find 'boring and unrewarding'. No, there was a

certain point which I thought much more interesting. 'Cats are cut out for space travel,' say our authors, claiming it's because of our wonderful sense of balance. Well, yes, I certainly agree! But why, I ask you, didn't NASA think of us straight away? There would be financial as well as scientific advantages in switching to cats as astronauts. For instance, space ships wouldn't have to be built on the Eiffel Tower dimensions familiar to us, and there'd be no need for enormous tent-sized space suits either. Everything human beings do in space – and we don't know exactly what it is they get up to there; very likely they just play games of Trivial Pursuit – everything they do could be done just as well by us. After all, our compulsive curiosity makes us ideal for hard work in the service of science. There'd be no need to worry about human physical flaws like a tendency to space sickness, because of our strong constitutions, and we'd soon put an end to the ridiculous spectacle of astronauts holding daily conversations with their wives. We could do all sorts of experiments. Do mice taste better in space, or do they become inedible? How long can a dog survive without oxygen after you push it out of the hatch into space? However, there are two problems still outstanding. First, the usual kind of food astronauts get, tubes of stuff made into paste, wouldn't do at all for space-cats. But I'm sure an intelligent tin-opening robot arm would solve that difficulty – only on condition that we get to programme it ourselves, of course. Second, there's the question of devising a suitable litter tray, because I really don't think I could last all the way to Neptune before doing the job and burying it.

With the increasing speed at which humans are mindlessly destroying this world, space travel is beginning to look more and more attractive to us cats anyway. It's about time we looked for new and unspoiled worlds. Who knows, perhaps we might find some under-developed people like those ancient Egyptians in the course of *our space flights, and we could civilise them for our own purposes. And then our glorious history would begin all over again. I have a suspicion that our original home lies outside this atmosphere anyway, and we've only paid Mother Earth a visit to plant the seed of genius here. They're talking about a manned flight to Mars in the near future. I hereby make my official application to go on it, and I will not conceal the fact that my fitness and ability to withstand stress are far superior to any biped's. Francis, the first cat in space . . . now I call that the ultimate target of evolution!*

CHAPTER 8

No
Two
Alike

Personality differences in cats

Cats are people on four legs, so it is fair to describe them in terms of a wise saying from the psychology textbooks: every human being is a little like all other human beings, a little like many other human beings, and a little like no other human being. On one level every cat is a universe to itself, an individual as unique as its genetic fingerprint. Even kittens from the same litter can react in astonishingly different ways in an identical situation, as the Austrian animal psychologist Ferdinand Brunner points out. Individual divergences in domestic pets are even greater than in their wild relations, because humans have bred certain feline personalities to their own liking: animals which no longer have to stand the test of a tough battle for survival as natural selection takes its course. In the wild, only those characteristics which help the organism to escape the Great Reaper and pass on its own heredity will last for long. In the natural world, your offspring are the only monuments you can leave behind you.

The psychologically unique nature of each cat's personality, says Brunner, is very clearly seen at feeding time. Some cats know exactly when they have had enough, while greedier animals will keep on and on until their overloaded digestive system brings up its contents. Others again are fussy, picking out only the best morsels and spurning the rest. Some cats are good mousers; other are good at hunting rats. There are cats of above average intelligence and others without much in the upper storey. There are cats of active and lethargic temperaments, the counterparts of those constitutional types in humans. And finally cat psychiatrists also see hyper-aggressive, sadistic and psychologically abnormal cats, corresponding to the psychopaths of human society. Perhaps there is even a serial killer cat somewhere in our midst, secretly murdering particularly attractive cats to make a coat of their skins.

There are countless systems for dividing humans (and cats) into various categories. Psychologists, naturally, are most interested in those statistically measurable qualities which are present in everyone to a different extent, for instance those personality traits on which the usual tests and questionnaires concentrate. People obviously like being pigeon-holed, as we can see from the popularity of magazine quizzes proposing increasingly weird and wonderful criteria. In the science of psychology, however, there is no agreement either on the really significant dimensions of the human personality, or on the criteria to be employed in comparing test subjects. Some new theory is devised almost every week, and the same confusing variety prevails in cat psychology.

While things like plants or makes of car can be classified with relative ease, personal qualities are defined in a very vague and murky sort of way. The idea of the four basic temperaments as defined by the ancient doctrine of the 'humours' has proved very tenacious. According to the Greek physician Hippocrates, the mixture of those fluids in the body is responsible for the differences in human nature. The 'melancholy' man is sad because black bile dominates his physical chemistry; sanguine people, on the other hand, are inclined to cheerfulness because red blood, the life-giving fluid, is dominant in them. Yellow bile makes the choleric man irascible and quick-tempered, while the relaxed phlegmatic gets his mellow disposition from the preponderance of viscid phlegm among his humours.

In various studies designed to discover the basic characteristics in which cats differed, the human assessors had to tick the qualities applying to individual animals. They all agreed on one point: it is nearly always easy to tell whether a cat is a shy introvert or a sociable extrovert, as the Canadian psychologist Robert E. Adamec has summed it up. The shy cat will seem upset and timid in a strange situation, or when meeting a strange person. On the other hand the opposite type, the extrovert cat, will venture boldly and fearlessly into any kind of new territory. Outgoing, confident cats immediately begin to explore surroundings strange to them, while the feline shrinking violet will creep into the nearest corner and sound out the terrain from a suitable distance. The inhibited and hesitant cat will also behave non-aggressively to large prey animals like rats, while posing as a ferocious lion to smaller prey like mice. If the small opponent, however, digs its heels in and offers resistance, the shy animal will retreat. Furthermore, defensive cats will pounce only on the relatively non-threatening backs of their prey, while prudently avoiding a head-on confrontation. If members of their own species shape up to them with threatening gestures, such cats will freeze into pillars of salt or take cover in the nearest refuge.

There are some surprising parallels with humans (and apes and monkeys), in whom the same two basic mental attitudes can be observed. The tendency to act timidly, described scientifically as 'inhibited behaviour', is seen as early as the beginning of the second year of life, says the Munich professor of psychology Jens Asendorpf. At this point inhibited and uninhibited children can be distinguished by their reactions in strange, new and unusual situations. Timid toddlers will fall suddenly silent, stop playing and cling to their mothers in distress when they are confronted by a strange person or strange objects. Their extrovert contemporaries, on the other hand, are not at all dismayed. They will quickly get off their mothers' laps and explore the new situation, undaunted.

In cats, says Adamec, timid characteristics appear between the first and second month of life. However, if we assume that one year in the cat's life is equivalent to seven human years, then the timing is just the same as in humans. According to the observations of American psychologists, moreover, about fifteen per cent of all children of the same age fall into the extreme groups of inhibited and uninhibited characters. The quota of strongly inhibited cats is also estimated to be about fifteen per cent.

The timid temperament, Asendorpf continues, remains very stable in human development. Shyness with strangers is as firmly established a trait as IQ, one of those characteristics of an individual which is least susceptible to change. Inhibited toddlers usually grow up to be inhibited schoolchildren who can easily be alarmed by people they do not know, and generally keep well out of harm's way because they have problems in approaching other people. However, a shy nature does not automatically brand a child social misfit, the scientist points out. Such children's difficulty in getting on with other people can be observed only if they are provoked by unfamiliar people or situations. Inhibitions do not prevent their mixing with familiar friends, so timid children may be as socially competent as their contemporaries. These children should be offered as stable an environment as possible, and their ability to build positive relationships with other people should be encouraged. A shy nature does not mean that its owner dislikes others: it is more likely that he or she is caught up in a conflict between approach and avoidance. Such people long for human contact, but the idea of actually making an approach terrifies them.

Again, the similarities with cats are considerable. Cats, too, usually retain their early characteristics all their lives, says the British geneticist Michael Mendl. Moreover, the cat's behaviour is not determined in every situation by its built-in disposition. Timid cats can play happily and uninhibitedly with people they know well, and they are not at all afraid of killing mice, says Adamec. We might therefore apply the

same educational recommendations to shy kittens as to shy human children.

As long ago as the days of ancient Greece it was proverbial to say that the eyes are the mirror of the soul. According to the American psychologist Jerome Kagan in his studies of several groups of children, a shy and introverted personality can actually to some extent be recognized from the colour of the retina. Shy boys and girls were about twice as likely to have blue eyes as brown eyes. The ratio of the two eye colours was exactly the other way round in the extrovert, uninhibited types. Eye colour depends on the amount of pigment (melanin) laid down in the iris. With low pigmentation the eyes will appear blue, while a high melanin content makes them brown. The other eye colours lie somewhere between these two extremes. Even in colloquial language the idea of being 'blue-eyed' is usually equated with innocence, naïvety and vulnerability. In cartoon films, comics and illustrations to children's fairy stories the gentle figures, like Cinderella, always have blue eyes, while 'harsh' characters such as the wicked stepmother are usually shown as brown-eyed.

So what about cats? According to the geneticist Mendl, blue-eyed white female cats of certain breeds are more timid than average, and this may be due to genetic causes. In fact the eyes of the cat may be all kinds of different colours, and odd-eyed kittens may sometimes be born. The most usual colours are yellow and green, but cats' eyes may also be blue, coppery pink or orange. The pigment shields the iris from excessive light, much as sun cream protects the human skin from excessive radiation. Consequently lack of pigment (blue eyes) may mean that the cat's sensitive eyes have a low light protection factor. Many people believe that cats with dark eyes feel better in general than cats with blue eyes.

We may ask why the melanin in the iris should change colour with different temperaments like a piece of litmus paper. The answer, according to Kagan, probably lies in the 'limbic system', a congested area at the base of the cerebral cortex which tests all stimuli reaching it for their significance. The limbic system also acts as a kind of alarm to interrupt all action in progress and bring the organism to a halt if it feels something is wrong. Scientists believe that at any given moment all higher forms of life are producing a viable 'world model' which contains hypotheses about the stimuli to be expected in the immediate future. All the information coming in through the sensory organs is compared with the prognosis by the comparator in the limbic system. The regular dripping of a tap can coincide so strongly with the internal world model that in the end you do not notice it at all. If it suddenly stops, however, its absence will produce a strong sense of discrepancy which alerts the comparator. Inhibited people and inhibited cats presumably have a comparator which is particularly prone to alarm, is made wary by the smallest deviation felt to be not quite right, and is ready to pull the emergency brakes on. The body is then flooded with stress hormones, the pulse beats frantically, and the brain, alerted to full wakefulness, thinks strenuously about the next steps to be taken.

Eye colour seems to be an indicator of the sensitivity of the body's own alarm system. Brown eyes indicate that the pituitary gland is shedding high concentrations of the hormone melanotropin, which in turn encourages the storing of melanin in the cells. Melanotropin, however, passes through various regions of the brain, particularly the limbic system, where it acts as a mild tranquilliser, dulling pain and making mental distress more tolerable. A low level of melanotropin, on the other hand, will be more likely to lead to blue eye colour and indicate a very active comparator, thus encouraging the development of a shy, introverted nature. Epileptic attacks, in cats as in humans, almost always originate in the limbic system. This centre has a long reach, and can upset the bio-electrical balance of excitement in the entire brain. If attacks are frequent, however, the limbic system becomes more and more excitable and sensitive, and tends to switch right off. So over the course of time, Adamec concludes, epileptic cats probably become even shyer and more timid.

There are some indications that genes are to a considerable extent responsible for passing on an introvert or extrovert temperament, principally through the paternal line. The early appearance of the first characteristics in the cat's infancy is very typical of an inherited disposition. The manner in which cats are handled by their owners, according to Bradshaw's initial findings, does not generally have any influence on their personality structures. Moreover, some breeds are much more inhibited (or outgoing) than others, and breeds are the direct expression of a genetic disposition. Possibly the basic tendency of a character can be slightly influenced one way or another by certain experiences, Adamec concedes. Cats who were frequently allowed to practise on injured or dazed prey when they were kittens will obviously be more inclined to drop some of their inborn inhibitions later. On the other hand, hereditary factors can even reverse the way in which certain experiences work. Extrovert kittens, for instance, will become even more outgoing and inclined to scuffle after competing with their siblings in the maternal nest. Timid cats, on the other hand, will have their natural shyness reinforced by early competition.

Obviously the laws of behavioural genetics established in studies of adopted children, twins and families also apply to cats, says Mendl. Behavioural genetics is a branch of research investigating groups of people with hereditary factors and environmental conditions which coincide to a precisely defined degree. Adoptive siblings, for instance, have no genes but a hundred per cent environmental factors in common. Identical twins who have grown up apart from each other, on the contrary, have a hundred per cent genetic factors but no environmental factors in common. Ordinary siblings come between the two, with fifty per cent of their genetic inheritance in common, and a hundred per cent of shared environmental factors. In ascertaining how much the people concerned resemble each other in the characteristic being studied, there are simple mathematical means of distinguishing between the power of the genes and the power of the environment.

Social and emotional personality traits, the latest studies suggest, are at least fifty per cent due to the genes. But that, say the behavioural geneticists, is not the surprising point. Even more crucial is the discovery that the 'classic' environmental factors such as education, social class etc., have almost no influence at all on development. Adoptive brothers and sisters with no genes in common remain as dissimilar after years of common upbringing as two individuals chosen at random from the general public. Identical twins who grow up in separate environments, however, will end up as much like each other as identical twins who grew up in the same family. The scientists concerned in these studies are claiming that the sociology textbooks should be entirely rewritten. All the circumstances that make people (for instance, identical twins) unlike each other are already there in the bosom of the family. This is why most siblings become so dissimilar over the course of time that their own parents are at a loss to understand it. In fact certain experiences can have a clear influence on character, but these, it seems, are those small, personal, idiosyncratic things that happen to everyone in his or her personal life. They may include chance meetings, personal friendships, even impressions gleaned from the mass media.

Genes, however, are doubly influential because they can reverse the effect of external experience, as mentioned above in relation to kittens competing in the nest. The organism is not just a passive receiver of external stimuli. Instead, it actively seeks out experiences and determines the tendency of their effect. Consequently, human beings (and cats) with a different genetic inheritance will perceive the same environment in a totally different way. To a passive and submissive son, an authoritarian father means something quite different from his significance to a rebellious and defiant one. The researchers have discovered that some people even attract certain 'fateful' experiences to themselves as a result of heredity. The number of blows of fate a person suffers during his life, according to the results of a new study of identical twins separated in infancy, is forty per cent determined by heredity. It may be, the psychologists conclude, that some people have natural characteristics whereby they actually bring certain unfortunate experiences upon themselves.

We might now perhaps ask naïvely why genetically conditioned differences of personality exist at all in cats (and humans), since certain characters (for instance, the extrovert type) seem at first glance to be more powerful than others. In theory the outgoing type of cat should catch more mice and rats, bring more offspring into the world, and end up wiping all the more timid members of its species off the face of the earth and out of the evolutionary process. But Charles Darwin himself, with brilliant insight, realised that the deeper meaning of sexual reproduction consists in the very fact that it produces offspring with a wide range of different qualities. Before the invention of sexuality, in the boring days before Madonna and 'adult' TV channels, when living creatures reproduced by non-sexual methods such as parthenogenesis, all offspring were identical with each other and their parent. However, experience shows that the secret of success lies in diversity. Ferdinand Merz, professor of psychology at Marburg University, explains that nature must keep producing variants, because life in its inexhaustible complexity makes very different demands. 'The environment of a species and thus the selective pressure on it do not remain constant in either space or time. Variants which are at a disadvantage in one area or one year may have the upper hand somewhere else or at some other time.'

Timid cats are obviously trying as hard as they can to avert all possible harm and dangers from themselves; their extrovert colleagues, on the other hand, are always ready for action. A questionnaire in a cat magazine suggested that coat colouring and breed play a part in deciding which tendency will predominate. The results of the questionnaire said that Siamese and (with some reservations) Persian cats were particularly spontaneous and uninhibited in their attitude to humans, while the Maine Coon was the breed most inclined to be withdrawn. Siamese scored sixty-eight points for approachability, the average for all breeds was fifty-one, and the Maine Coon scored just forty-four. Judged by coat colouring, the highest scorers for approachability were tabby cats (seventy-three points), sealpoints (seventy-two points) and blues (sixty-nine points) , while tortoiseshells (forty-one points) and grey cats (forty-five points) were more inclined to be shy of human beings. The findings suggested that Siamese were least interested in inanimate objects and Chartreux cats (a French breed similar to the British Blue) most interested in them.

It is easy to see that both the timid and the extrovert mentalities could have advantages and disadvantages, depending on circumstances. A tendency to play safe the whole time may preserve a cat from making a number of bad mistakes, the kind which costs an extrovert cat its life. But shy animals are not the pace-setters and pioneers who will discover new homes and new sources of food. Outgoing cats usually take the lead – and they probably, alas, lead the way to the eternal hunting grounds as well.

The fact that different types of characters have their own strengths and weaknesses, according to Merz, shows up in our own cousins the apes. Defending the home range is exclusively the preserve of adult male apes; during travelling and changes of location, however, the troop is usually led by adult females. Finally, experiments have also shown that very aggressive mice are dominant and produce more offspring in a predictable and stable environment; their more pacific colleagues, on the other hand, are more successful in times of change and alteration. Many behavioural strategies work only as long as they are employed by a limited number of individuals. There can never be more than a few really successful fare dodgers and tax evaders; if the same strategy were employed by honest citizens the entire system would fall apart. Comparative behavioural science, or ethology, has a special discipline known as games theory which explores the question of the distribution whereby various strategies form a stable system.

Comments by Francis

Too good to be true, if you ask me. What's too good to be true? Why, telling us that the members of my species are all different individuals, whereas unfortunately they resemble each other as closely as one Big Mac resembles another – and I don't pick that comparison idly, either. Just as human beings go through a deplorable change in the course of their lives, from go-ahead, energetic young things to couch potatoes seated in front of the box or behind the bar, so most of my kind pursue a similarly shameful career, changing from universally feared mouser to obsessive guardian of a comfortable cushion by a radiator. Isn't it a fact that only a tiny, right-minded remnant of us will retain the life-style of a wild animal all our lives? Isn't it a fact that our bold hunting of those revolting creatures, rats,

our great battles with the local toms, from which we always of course emerge victorious, our nights of love with the Siamese queen next door, all take place mainly in our dreams once we've fallen asleep from over-eating beside our bowls? The temptations of comfort aren't just the scourge of mankind, they also ruin the noble nature of the feline race. Close contact with all human mod cons makes us fat, lazy and boring. It really is enough to make a cat laugh to think that a fat feline who can barely drag his huge hindquarters from one feeding trough to the next was once worshipped by whole nations. Let's admit it: bourgeois conformity isn't just a term invented by outsiders in search of an insult for the majority, but a dangerous sickness which sooner or later levels out all characters, however unique, to fit the usual model. Overnight, the wild rock star who changes women more often than his underpants, and lives solely on drugs, will start helping his wife with the Christmas shopping and getting high on nothing more exciting than tea. You find the erstwhile revolutionary working in the Department of Social Security, peacefully blowing the dust off files, a civil servant with a pension plan and a monthly salary and bonus scheme. That's why personality differences are so important, not just in humans but also in such higher life forms as Felidae. I suspect that the pressures of the modern age and the temptation it offers us to avoid suffering will make us all identical in the end. There are exceptions, of course. Such as Mozart, and James Dean, and me.

CHAPTER 9

Clever
Cats

The cat's intelligence
and learning ability

Most cat owners who observe their pets closely get the impression that the animals are pursuing a course of planned activity, with certain ends in view, and that forethought rules their actions. Humans in general have a tendency to project their own mental processes on to animate and indeed inanimate nature. Given sufficient imagination, we can project ourselves into plants, animals and even inanimate material objects, as Patrick Bateson and Dennis Turner point out in their book on cat behaviour. The wish to experience what it is like to be something else is very strong, and is frequently rewarded by a better understanding of those other things in themselves. Consequently, even 'hard' natural scientists will sometimes indulge in teleological thinking, speaking as if particles, molecules and complex systems could act with purposeful intent. There is even a special philosophical trend called panpsychism which claims that consciousness is not a prerogative of the human brain. Even the simplest and lowest components of the universe, according to this school of thought, have the mental aura, albeit in low concentration, that will rise to ever greater intellectual heights in the process of evolution.

We can never prove objectively that cats have a conscious ego, but then again, the consciousness of other people must always remain a supposition too, if a plausible one. Theoretically, other people could be mindless robots merely putting on a very good imitation of being human. At present an intensive discussion is being conducted by ethologists about the point at which one can say that a living creature has thought and consciousness. Obviously language, that triumphant achievement of *Homo sapiens*, is no criterion, or we would have to say that deaf mute people were unable to think. As early as the turn of the century the sociologist L. T. Hobhouse was voicing the possibility that his cat Lonce had higher mental gifts. The cat had developed the habit of lifting the doormat and letting it fall back to knock against the closed door if it wanted to get into the sitting-room. It is possible that the cat combined a series of abstract notions (doors can be opened; you can draw attention to yourself by making a noise; etc.) to make up one brilliant idea. Or perhaps it simply lifted the doormat once by chance and was then conditioned by the pleasing consequences.

A characteristic of lower, mentally backward forms of life in their natural setting is that they will not develop activities of any kind unless they are induced to do so by strong external stimuli or instinctive drives (e.g. hunger or thirst). Most organisms which do not have a highly developed cerebral cortex react mechanically to stimuli. There is no doubt that the cat is at the opposite end of this evolutionary ladder, as everyday observations prove. Even if it is dozing comfortably by the radiator, the cat will start up now and then, for no obvious reason, to follow the demands of some mysterious impulse. It could be just to go and inspect the food dish critically, rather than to eat from it, and then, if all is well, to return to its slumbers with its mind set at rest. If you divert the cat's attention with a game of some kind before it has put its *idée fixe* into practice, the original impulse will often be forgotten, and the cat will go straight back to sleep. But that would imply that from the start the animal had only some vague, partially formed idea in its head, and was not impelled by strong stimuli or instinctive drives. After all, crackpot notions lie at the root of the development of all higher natures.

Organisms with low mental ability never see beyond the horizon of the moment and are slavishly fixed on the present. The parts of the brain which were most extended in the development towards becoming human are those that deal with the planning of future projects. Because of this, we chalk it up to the credit of our closest relations, the apes, that they too have the knack of anticipation and forward planning. African chimpanzees, for instance, will go on very long journeys to reach the granite stones they use for cracking certain tasty nuts. Such a project is based not only on forethought and an understanding of the use of tools, but also

on the ability to keep an abstract aim (finding stones) in mind while the chimpanzees have to deal with quite different demands (finding the way). Cats, however, will often persist in sitting by a hole in which a mouse has taken refuge for a very long time. In fact that action could be taken as a symbol of the essence of the feline nature. Cats can obviously rise to considerable mental heights, at least when they want to satisfy their lower instincts,

St Francis's ability to talk to the animals is not something to which ordinary sinful humans can aspire. In the era of computers and microchips, however, the legendary wish to do just that may be more likely to turn to the idea of some electronic device enabling us to 'read' the thoughts in our pets' minds. The closest approximation to such a consciousness-detector is probably the electroencephalograph or EEG, which measures the electrical activity of the brain. The curves derived by the standard EEG from the surface of the skull, however, are not suitable for subtle mental diagnosis. They reflect the coarse, undifferentiated activity of billions of pulsing nerve cells, and rather resemble the wild roar to be heard in a football stadium. The normal EEG, then, picks up only very coarse and elementary psychic conditions such as being awake, being asleep, having a fit or being brain-dead – much as one can tell whether the noise in the football stadium denotes victory or defeat. If we want to receive detailed messages – or even thoughts? – from the garbled bio-electrical language of the EEG, we shall have to filter out its extremely subtle event-related potentials with high-powered computers. This is more like placing a microphone right in front of a small group of football fans to listen in to what they are saying.

Event-related potentials are the waves produced at certain points in the brain when the organism is mentally processing very distinct impressions such as sounds, flashes of light or words. One of the most interesting potentials of this kind is the P300 wave. This peak in the EEG always appears when information is being arranged in an intellectually complex manner. If test subjects are offered certain stimuli such as humming notes or flashes of light in monotonous repetition, and then an unexpected note (or image) is suddenly introduced, the intrusive element engenders a greater P300 potential. The omission of an anticipated stimulus will provoke even more violent after-tremors in the brain. The curves show up most strongly if the test subjects are made to think about the stimuli presented to them: if, for instance, they have to pick out from a sequence of words any which rhyme with 'cake' or any which refer to a living thing. The American psychologist Donald R. Griffin concludes that the results suggest that event-related potentials provide a rough gauge of conscious thought. The sharp curves are greatly reduced or become entirely invisible if the test subject stops paying attention to the exercise.

By now the reader may be wondering impatiently whether anyone has investigated cats (and other animals) for these obscure bio-signals. They have. It was found possible to establish the presence of the P300-wave in both apes and cats. The feline brain produces the give-away signs if a certain relevant tone is heard among several neutral tones. This is called the 'eccentric exceptional stimulus' and can mean, for instance, that if the cat now presses a button it will get food, or that it must now withdraw its paw if it is not to receive a harmless electric shock. Griffin sees this as being at least an indication that cats are capable of conscious thought. His colleagues, however, are more cautious, and prefer the more diplomatic concept of cognition. Perhaps the curves only mean that new and unexpected stimuli require more work (i.e. electric current) from the brain. And even the event-related potentials of other human beings are no definitive proof of consciousness. Such curves might even be found in mice if the researchers went on long enough.

Konrad Lorenz, the founding father of German ethology, famous for his studies of geese, has vigorously rejected the legend of the cat's duplicity. 'There are few other animals in whose faces those who know them can so clearly read their present moods.' Lorenz insisted that the body and face of the cat nearly always provide a faithful account of what is going on inside it, and what kind of behaviour should be expected in the immediate future. A slight suggestion of suspicion – it need not even be fear – and those innocent round eyes will become rather elongated and slanting. Lorenz may not have been at his most penetrating when he made this 'honesty' an excuse for casting aspersions on the cat's mental competence: 'I would not, however, call the cat's inability to deceive meritorious, but I do consider it a sign of the dog's higher intelligence that it can do just that.' Lorenz follows up this statement with an anecdote about his old dog Bully, whose sight was failing, so that he often barked angrily at his master when he came home. When he recognised his mistake the dog used to feel painful embarrassment. After a few such lapses, however, he developed a curious habit: he would come running up, barking, would recognise his master, stop for a moment, and then run on, still barking, so as to end up yapping furiously at an imaginary enemy on the other side of the wall. Obviously the clever animal had worked out an excuse for his unfortunate *faux pas*.

How exactly can deceitful communication be considered a sign of high intelligence? Most animal species are inclined to hide their intentions from a rival in order to give themselves an advantage in any forthcoming confrontation. Lying, however, makes greater demands on the intellect than honesty. A 'forked tongue' must perform several mental operations at once if it is going to deceive anyone. It must keep what it knows to be the truth at the back of its mind, and simultaneously convey a fictitious statement credibly ('It's that dog on the other side of the wall I mean'). This takes more mental effort, and with suitable instruments that effort can be detected in the liar's vegetative nervous system. The device popularly and imprecisely known as a lie detector is really registering the effort involved in distorting the truth, rather than showing up a guilty conscience.

The best liars – apart from human beings – are apes and monkeys, and their dishonesty too is regarded as a proof of their high intelligence, as the Göttingen anthropologist Volker Sommer describes in his fascinating book *Lob der Lüge* [*In Praise of Lying*], a survey of the natural history of deception and lying. Baboons who see a physically superior rival making off with a delicious item of food, for instance, will sometimes raise the alarm for no good reason, using the baboon's typical warning cry, and will steal the rival's find when he runs off, fearing a tiger. Subordinate gorillas and chimpanzees who spot some hidden delicacy while they are with the main body of the troop will frequently pretend to have seen nothing, but will return to the place where they can find the hidden delicacy later, and alone. Apes at the lower end of the pecking order, threatened by a higher-ranking animal, will sometimes stare with pretended horror into a corner as if they saw some monster there. This diversionary tactic frequently works and provides the moment of respite necessary for successful flight. The gibbons, who live a strictly monogamous life, sing morning duets which presumably send a message to the neighbours saying, 'This territory is ours!' A widowed female gibbon, however, was heard singing solos which resembled the part once performed by her dead consort. She obviously wanted to give the impression that both adults were still in possession of their site.

Cats are not mentioned in Sommer's book on lying, but they are not straightforward just because they lack the wit to lie. The current view is that cats communicate honestly because doing so favours survival in their natural ecological niche. As almost all cats have enough power to bring down living creatures of their own order of size, aggression between members of the same species is mortally dangerous. The honest and unmistakable meaning of feline language has thus presumably developed to keep the risks of a fierce showdown as low as possible. In principle, the cat must try to avoid injuries and prevent the escalation of aggression.

Leaving that aspect aside, dishonesty, lies and pretence are more common among species which, like dogs, apes and humans, live in a relatively rigid social organisation. Many of our customary social conventions such as politeness, tact and good manners are at bottom ritualised forms of lying, now acting as lubricants so that we can live together without friction. That is why we sometimes feel so envious of the cat, who could not care less about social conventions, at least in its original solitary life-style.

Of course the cat has not the slightest reason to deviate from the path of virtue in its dealings with mice and other mobile foodstuffs. The only times members of the cat family have been detected employing cunning and deception have been in connection with larger prey animals. Some observers believe, for instance, that the tiger is able to imitate the rutting cry of deer and thus lure them to their doom. However, it would be easier to believe this of leopards, who are the most vocal of all the big cats and produce a particularly wide range of sounds. Other people claim to have seen the jaguar dangling its twitching tail in water as a bait, luring fish and then scooping them into its mouth with its big paws. These tactics have even won the jaguar a place in a book of records of the animal kingdom as the largest mammalian angler. The only beast of prey who fishes for the benefit of human beings, however, is the serval cat. The serval, about 1.10 metres in size, lives in West and Central Africa and is trained to fish while young. This faithful helper will snatch fish weighing up to five kilograms from the water with its swift paws. Of all beasts of prey, only the cheetah has been used for hunting on land; the Sumerians were hunting with cheetahs three thousand years before Christ.

In another passage, Konrad Lorenz quotes the example of a

dog he knew who always limped and pretended to have a lame leg when he wanted to attract the attention and sympathy of his human companions. Some while earlier this dog had in fact suffered an injury, but it had long since healed. He was therefore only pretending to be injured to get those secondary advantages of illness he had come to value. In Lorenz's opinion, only dogs are able to perform such a cunning act. However, the American cat expert Paul Corey does not agree; he has seen his cats putting on a similar performance. He mentions in particular the case of his black and white cat Charles, who had hurt his back as a kitten. Years later, long after the injury was healed, Charles would still begin limping the moment he wanted attention. Corey and his wife only had to say 'Poor Charles!' and the small actor would give a highly professional performance.

Corey also claims that one of his cats could utter a makeshift imitation of the word 'out' when it wanted to get out of doors. One imagines that this cat must have been a Siamese, since Siamese are known to be the most talkative of domestic cats. Finally, there was a dog on American television who advertised a brand of beer by muttering 'I like Bud'.

The belief that the intellectual gifts of different species might be assessed by a single standard – much as the performance of an engine is expressed in horse-power – is now very outmoded. All organisms, by today's way of thinking, have whatever kind of intelligence will be most useful to them in their ecological niche; we cannot judge the intelligence of cats and dogs by the same standard. Even the intelligence of several humans probably cannot be reduced to a single common denominator, the famous IQ or intelligence quotient. The tests involved in measuring IQ comprise a series of mental games which are supposed to be representative of intelligent behaviour in daily life. The method is certainly reliable in that much the same score will be obtained in several repetitions of tests, but their validity, or statistical application in real life, leaves much to be desired. IQ may make accurate predictions about scholastic achievement, but it cannot forecast success in a person's later career. Moreover, IQ is very strongly tailored to the special capabilities of mathematicians and other eggheads, while it ignores practical intelligence. Consequently a number of psychologists believe that we really have various distinct kinds of intelligence. These multiple intelligences derive from different requirements in our evolutionary past and display independent variation from each other. That is to say, you can be a genius in one area and a total idiot in another. Linguistic intelligence, for instance, shows in the skilful use of language, spatial intelligence in navigation and the visual arts, interpersonal intelligence in a subtle feeling for the workings of other people's minds. We have probably not even begun to discover the complete range of multiple intelligences.

Where the IQ is not very high, no great revelations can be expected of the EQ either. EQ stands for 'encephalisation quotient', a measurement of the amount of brain power left over after the immediate demands made on the brain to control basic body functions are taken into account. We could call it the luxury area of the brain, available for mental study of the world. The cat has a higher EQ than any rodent, but a lower one than the dog, which has an EQ twenty-five per cent greater. In the dog, however, the extremely large olfactory

area of the brain is very marked and does not necessarily function in an 'intellectual' way. The domestic cat's brain may be smaller than the brains of its wild forebears, but we need not conclude that it is therefore less intelligent. It is simply that domestic pets are no longer as watchful, constantly alert and ready for flight as in the wild. On the other hand, their learning abilities – and sex drive – have clearly increased.

A new theory which has recently found many adherents sees what it describes as ecological surplus capacities as the nub of the matter. This theory states that all organisms have the mental capacity necessary to overcome the problems typical of their ecological niche. Beyond that capacity there is a greater or lesser amount of extra intelligence which helps them to solve new and unexpected problems. By this criterion the domestic cat is a truly intelligent animal, since it is one of the most adaptable of mammals. It can be found living in areas from the sub-arctic islands to large and busy cities, and feline population density varies from one animal to two thousand individuals per square kilometre. The cat is also extremely flexible in its relationship to humans; contact begins at nil, on uninhabited islands, and goes up to living shoulder to shoulder in permanent close proximity in a modern big city household. The cat can make the jump from the wilderness to civilised life and back again within a few generations. In line with that ability, cats are also very quick to master certain tricks which were never foreseen by their pre-programmed instincts, but which improve the quality of life in civilised surroundings. They can open doors when the handle is close enough for them to jump up and reach it; they find out how to quench their thirst from a dripping tap; and they discover that dried cat-food can be extracted from its box with a paw.

In the early days of experimental psychology cats were popular and much used as guinea pigs. For instance, they soon learned how to get out of a puzzle-box, quickly discovering how to work the latch that would open the box even if they had to manoeuvre wooden catches at the same time. Later on, when the task set them was merely a matter of working a lever to obtain food, cats proved disappointingly unwilling to perform and were replaced by rodents and pigeons. However, such experiments do not prove that cats are stupid: in natural conditions they eat moving, rustling, intelligent prey and not, like pigeons, 'dead' grain. Hunting intelligent food makes very high demands on the hunter's brain; he must not only spy out the location of the prey but also prevent it from seeing through his own behaviour. That may be why cats seem to be bad at performing simple and monotonous tasks, while they can solve other problems standing on their heads.

All the cat's brain functions and thought processes are very well adapted to the needs of a solitary beast of prey which must analyse the situation at lightning speed while hunting, and must always keep a step ahead of its prey animal. This fact will sometimes produce bizarre results in elementary learning processes such as Pavlovian conditioning. In one experiment, the 'simple' lesson was to learn that after the cat heard a certain sound it might expect to find a helping of food in another part of the room. The cat in the experiment did not go straight to the source of the reward, as a dog, pigeon or mouse would, but inspected the loudspeaker and its sur-

roundings intently; after a while, being a cat with a mind of its own, it ostentatiously ignored the food offered but excitedly chewed the source of the sound. A hunter, after all, must know which way his prey is going at any time. A dog will immediately come when called; a cat, on the other hand, usually prefers to find out what all the fuss is in aid of first.

Early educational psychologists of the behaviourist school hoped to discover that almost any species of animal could be trained to behave in any way, however outlandish, if offered suitable rewards. Their guiding principle was the law of effect: every kind of behaviour is determined by its consequences. The organism does things that have desirable consequences while omitting to perform activities with an undesirable end result. However, it soon transpired that cats could be much more easily induced to perform those actions that are a natural part of the hunting process. For instance, they will readily pull back a lever with the paw, an action which is not unlike reaching for a prey animal hiding behind some projection, but they find it much more difficult simply to push a lever forward to get a reward. Edward Thorndike, the founding father of this school of psychology, discovered that the cat will never learn the knack of certain things. For instance, if it happens to set off the reward mechanism accidentally with its tail, it will still never pick up the idea of the success principle. Living creatures of different species are obviously pre-programmed to catch on most quickly to those principles which would be clearly advantageous in their natural environment, but they get nowhere in learning other lessons which have no ecological relevance to them.

One of the milestones in the intellectual development of

small children is an understanding of 'object permanence'. This means grasping the idea that an object still exists when it is hidden from sight. The test for an advanced form of object permanence consists in moving some interesting item such as a toy from one hiding place to another before the eyes of the small children involved. In these circumstances, children who have not yet developed this capacity very far will look for the item in its original hiding place and be disappointed. When the same test was tried with cats, those clever animals immediately went to the 'right' place. However, if the researcher had surreptitiously removed the object of their interest again so that its scent would provide no clues, a suspicious cat kept searching, digging and sniffing busily at the scene of the crime. One can imagine the infuriating effect on a cat when a mouse which was visible a moment ago suddenly seems to dissolve into thin air.

The cat shares with the most intelligent of all mammals the ability to make a cognitive map of a given terrain in its head. Lower mammals orientate themselves almost exclusively by landmarks when finding their way about a certain area: turn right at the first tree, then left at the bush with the funny smell. If the bush has disappeared, they are baffled. Once a cat has got a route into its head, however, it forms a mental simulation of the area and can thus 'read' short cuts in the mind's eye. 'Last time I passed the tree first, then the bush; if I go across the field I can get there much faster.'

The quickest and most effective form of learning is learning by observation. An individual immediately 'imitates' the entire activity of a model successfully performing a certain complex task. Even as kittens, cats learn by observation, and there are indications that adult cats learn clever tricks (such as how to open a door) from other cats. If they should ever learn by observation how to open tins, a sizeable wedge might be driven into the symbiotic relationship between cats and humans.

Final comments by Francis

What a laugh! To think of all those eggheads with their silly intelligence tests going to all that trouble, just to prove that we're not stupid! My dear good friends, why all this fuss? Haven't you really got anything better to do? Considering the state your world is in, I'd have thought you had more pressing worries. I mean, have you ever stopped to think that in your society any idiot is allowed to vote, thus exerting influence on the social order? How about certifying that those simple minds actually have intelligent consciousness before letting them near the ballot box? Well, never mind that: the impertinent remarks made by the authors show that humans still have difficulty in admitting that other species have any kind of intelligence. I've no basic objection to that. Let them remain in ignorance about my kind for all I care. But they might wonder in future just why we have such wonderful eyes, ears and noses, whether we can penetrate other dimensions with our extrasensory powers, and whether we may not be fooling them behind their backs. I am firmly opposed to human endeavours to demystify and desecrate everything mysterious and holy with their logical acrobatics. Let their monks get married and even keep harems for all I care, let their popes be women holding office by turn on a democratic basis. But kindly spare us, the true gods of this word, such newfangled nonsense. No intelligence test can measure our intelligence, no historian can fathom the mystery of our origins. *Comparisons with other species are bound to fail miserably, because comparing mere serviceable beings with creatures of genius is like comparing bricks with diamonds.*

So let us remain a mystery to ourselves and the unthinking human world. My kind have survived many a dark age, many a despotic rule and many a bloodthirsty superstition, and here we still are, more charming and fascinating than ever. And believe you me, we will continue to survive. However, I can safely assure our two irreverent authors of one thing. You needn't be afraid of the problems if we ever find out how to open tins. Between you and me, we've had the knack for ages. But why lower ourselves to perform this menial task? You two-legged tin-openers are really much better at it than we are.

Bibliography

Books

Ackerman, Diane: *A Natural History of the Senses*. London 1990.

Allen, Eric *et al.*: *Die Katze*. Hamburg 1987.

Anon.: *Katzen*. Munich 1990.

Asendorpf, Jens: *Soziale Gehemmtheit und ihre Entwicklung*. Berlin etc. 1989.

Bertsch, Andreas: *Wie Pflanzen und Tiere sich ernähren*. Ravensburg 1980.

Bradshaw, John W.S.: *The Behaviour of the Domestic Cat*. London 1992. Very profound and expert monograph on the behaviour of the cat, drawing fully on present knowledge of the subject and assuming at least an educated lay reader's state of knowledge.

Brunner, Ferdinand: *Die Unverstandene Katze*. Melsungen 1989.

Burger, I.H. and Rivers, J.P.W. (eds.): *Nutrition of the Dog and Cat*. Cambridge 1989.

Caras, Roger A.: *A Cat is Watching*. New York etc. 1991. A sympathetic study giving a vivid idea of how the cat experiences human beings and the world.

Caras, Roger A.: *A Celebration of the Cat*. New York and London 1989. A passionate declaration of love for the cat. With remarkable intuition, Caras sums up what cat and man have meant to each other in history so far.

Chinery, Michael: *Killers of the Wild*. London 1979.

Corey, Paul: *Do Cats Think?* Illinois 1991. A vivid collection of anecdotal accounts which well illustrate the high intellectual capacity of the domestic cat.

Downer, John: *Supersense: Perception in the Animal World*. London 1988.

Fleming, Bill and Petersen-Fleming, Judy: *The Tiger on Your Couch*. New York 1992.

Fogle, Bruce: *The Cat's Mind*. London 1991.

Fox, Michael W.: *Understanding Your Cat*. New York 1992. A very competent manual by a leading American student of cat behaviour, embracing all areas, from general health through the world of the senses to psychological well-being.

Gerber, Bärbel: *Katzen*. Niederhausen 1990.

Gettings, Frank: *The Secret Lore of the Cat*. New York 1992.

Griffin, Donald R.: *Animal Thinking*. Cambridge (Mass.) and London 1984.

Herre, Wolf and Röhrs, Manfred: *Haustiere zoologisch betrachtet*. Stuttgart and New York 1990. A standard zoological work providing insight into the history of our pets' domestication, their bodies and their behaviour.

Hoffmann, E.T.A.: *Lebensansichten des Kater Murr* [The Philosophy of Life of Murr the Cat]. First edition, Vol. 1 1819; Vol. 2 1821. The delightful story of a tom cat who dips his claws in the inkwell and writes his own life history on paper 'illuminated at night by the phosphorus of my eyes'. Torn between an enthusiasm for philosophy on the one hand and the lower pleasures of animal life on the other, Murr is a sympathetic image of the split in the feline soul, his story shot through by the ironic undertones of the great Romantic novelist.

Holland, Barbara: *The Name of the Cat*. New York and London 1988.

Hue, Jean-Louis: *Katzen. Eine Liebeserklärung*. Düsseldorf 1984.

Jones, Margaret (ed.): *Big Cats*. Hamburg 1992. A lavishly produced picture book with breathtaking photographs of the large wild relatives of our tame domestic tiger. In addition there are many interesting textual passages by leading authorities on the subject, giving an authoritative survey of the way of life of these majestic beasts of prey.

Kitchener, Andrew: *The Natural History of the Wild Cats*. New York 1991.

Klever, Ulrich: *Knaurrs großes Katzenbuch*. Munich 1985. A German writer, gourmet and cat-lover, who has written an appealing, entertaining and yet always informative standard work on the animal, displaying both fascination with cats and a wealth of knowledge.

Kühl, Christian: *Mensch und Katze*. Geneva and Munich 1993.

Kunkel, Paul: *How to Toilet-Train Your Cat*. New York 1991.

Leyhausen, Paul: *Katzen*, Berlin 1979, English tr. *Cat Behavior*, New York 1979. Two decades after its first appearance this monograph is still a milestone of empirical cat research. Leyhausen was probably the first to turn a scientist's acute and sober gift for observation on a living creature previously viewed mainly through the eyes of dreamers, mystics and poets.

Lorenz, Konrad: *Man Meets Dog*. London 1977.

Makowski, Henry: *Neuer Kurs für Noahs Arche*. Munich 1986.

Mann, Daniel: *Rekorde der Tierwelt*. Munich and Berlin 1979.

Manolson, Frank: *C is for Cat*. London 1979.

Montagu, Ashley: *Touching: The Human Significance of the Skin*. New York and London 1971.

Morris, Desmond: *Catwatching*. London 1986. The two bestsellers by Desmond Morris, dealing in question-and-answer form with the most interesting and fascinating aspects of the feline world as if turning a spotlight on them, have considerably increased general knowledge about our household pets. The writer, a scientist who has tackled a number of exciting aspects of evolution and ethology in his many bestselling books, sometimes allows his imagination to run away with him; when he does so, the magic wand of analogy is occasionally waved too vigorously, and the result is – well, pure feline magic, but always enjoyable.

Morris, Desmond: *Catlore*. London 1987. See remarks on Morris's other book above.

Neville, Peter: *Do Cats Need Shrinks?* London 1990. An entertaining survey of various neuroses and behavioural disturbances of the cat, together with many suggestions for successful therapy.

Piechocki, Rudolf: *Die Wildkatze*. Everything worth knowing about the shy wild-cat of the European forests, which can sometimes mate with softer town-dwelling cats, and in its own harsh environment is always on the very brink of survival.

Raiberti, Giovanni: *Die Katze*. Vienna 1989.

Sayer, Angela: *The Complete Book of the Cat*. London 1984.

Scär, Rosemarie: *Die Hauskatze*. Stuttgart 1989.

Schmitt, Christa: *Die Katze in Sprichwort und Redensart*. Stuttgart 1988.

Siegel, Ronald K.: *Intoxication*. New York and London 1989. A fascinating and inspired natural history of intoxication.

Sinclair, Sandra: *How Animals See*. Sydney 1985.

Sommer, Volker: *Lob der Lüge*. Munich 1992.

Streitenfeld, Regina and Dirk: *Katzen Kultur*. Hamburg 1987. A fascinating exploration of the depiction of the cat in advertising and popular culture, with many graphic delights.

Tabor, Roger: *The Wild Life of the Domestic Cat*. London 1983. A clever book about the behaviour of the cat, uniting a gift for painstaking observation with creative and original interpretation.

Taylor, David: *The Ultimate Cat Book*. London 1989. A survey of the body, nature and mind of the cat, written in a very bright and lively way. It will stand comparison with the best works of this kind.

Taylor, David: *You and Your Cat*. London 1986.

Thorne, C. (ed.): *The Waltham Book of Dog and Cat Behaviour*. Oxford 1992.

Turner, Dennis C.: *Das sind Katzen*. Stuttgart and Vienna 1988. Compact, accessible edition of the volume edited by Turner and Bateson.

Turner, Dennis and Bateson, Patrick (eds.): *The Domestic Cat: The Biology of Its Behaviour*. Cambridge 1986. The ultimate scientific standard work on the behaviour and characteristics of the cat, arising from the symposium of a large scientific congress. All leading specialists in the field contributed up-to-date articles on such basic aspects of the subject as hunting, sexuality and play.

Voland, Eckart: *Grundriß der Soziobiologie*. Stuttgart and Jena 1993.

Wright, Michael and Walters, Sally (eds.): *Die Katze*. Munich 1985. A basic manual containing an encyclopedic wealth of information and written by many leading experts.

Contributions to collected works, journals and leaflets

Adamec, Robert E.: 'Anxious Personality in the Cat.' In: Carroll, Bernard J. and Barrett, James E. (eds): *Psychopathology and the Brain*. New York 1991. A scientific treatise on the biological mechanisms which can lead to many cats having shy temperaments while others appear outgoing and relaxed.

Anon.: 'Ernährung und Fettsucht bei der Katze.' *Katzen*, No. 5 (1985), pp. 5–8.

Anon.: 'Bei Fremden tanzt die Siam aus der Reihe.' *Geliebte Katze*, No. 7 (1993), pp. 16–17.

Anon.: 'Purr-tenance and Physiology.' *The Lancet, No. 339* (1992), p. 1578.

Anon.: 'Das Schnurren der Katze hilft gegen das Alleinesein.' *Katzen*, No. 4, 1991, no p. number.

Anon.: 'Verhaltensweisen von Katzen bei der Nahrungsaufnahme.' *Katzen*, No. 1 (1988), pp. 24–8.

Anon.: 'Was ist eine Katze?' *Katzen*, 20 (1990), No. 3, pp. 6–8.

Arluke, Arnold, and Sax, Borian: 'Understanding Nazi Animal Protection and the Holocaust.' *Anthrozoös*, No. 5 (1992), pp. 6–31

Aronson, Lester B. and Cooper, Madeline L.: 'Penile Spines of the Domestic Cat.' *Anatomical Record*, No. 157 (1967), pp. 71–8. An anatomical investigation of the structure and function of the spines on the male cat's penis.

Bartoshuk, Linda *et al.*: 'Taste of Water in the Cat.' *Science*, No. 171 (1971), pp. 699–701.

Bergler, Reinhold: 'Die Beziehung zwischen Mensch und Katze.' *Katzen*, No. 6, 1987, pp. 5–10.

Braekevelt, Charlie R.: 'Fine Structure of the Feline Tapetum Lucidum.' *Anatomy, Histology, Embryology*, No. 105 (1990), pp. 97–105.

Brown, R.G.: 'Making Pet Foods.' *Canadian Veterinary Journal*, No. 29 (1988), pp. 465–6.

Buffington, Tony: 'Meeting the Nutritional Needs of Your Feline Patients.' *Veterinary Medicine*, No. 86 (1991), pp. 720–27.

Bulla, Gisela: *Katzen Lexikon*, Reinbek 1986.

Caro, T.M. and Hauser, M.D.: 'Is there Teaching in Non-human Animals?' *The Quarterly Review of Biology*, No. 67 (1992), p. 151ff.

Cherfas, Jeremy: 'How to Thrill Your Cat this Christmas.' *New Scientist*, No. 116 (1987), pp. 42–5.

Corbin, James E.: 'Inedible Meat, Poultry and Fish By-Products in Pet Foods.' In: Pearson, A.M., and Dutson, T.R. (eds.): *Inedible Meat By-Products (Advances in Meat Research*, vol. 8). London and New York 1992.

Crane, S.W.: 'Occurrence and Management of Obesity in Companion Animals.' *Journal of Small Animal Practice*, No. 32 (1991), pp. 275–82.

Effem: 'Heimtierfertignahrung: Qualitätssicherung.' Verden, no date.

Effem: 'Katzenernährung.' Verden 1992.

'ENIGMA-Untersuchung.' *Katzen*, No. 5 (1991), pp. 8–11.

Frank, Fritz and Loos-Frank, Brigitte: 'Die Beute einer Hauskatze (*Felis catus*) aus 10 Jahren.' *Bonner zoologische Beiträge*, No. 40 (1989), pp. 205–15.

Hart, Benjamin L. and Leedy, Mitzi G.: 'Stimulus and Hormonal Determinants of Flehmen Behavior in Cats.' *Hormones and Behavior*, No. 21 (1987), pp. 44–52.

Herrscher, Rüdiger: 'Wohlgenährte Katzen bleiben länger gesund.' *Katzen extra Spezial*, No. 2 (1992), pp. 39–43.

Houpt, Katherine A. *et al.*: 'A Tuna Fish Diet Influences Cat Behavior.' *Journal of Toxicology and Environmental Health*, No. 24 (1988), pp. 161–72.

Kane, Edward: 'Feeding Behaviour of the Cat.' In: Burger, I.H. and Rivers, J.P.W.: *Nutrition of the Dog and Cat*, Cambridge etc. 1989.

Kania, Willy: 'Sind unsere Katzen intelligent?' *Katzen*, No. 3, 1990, pp. 10–14.

Leibetseder, Josef: 'Energiereduzierte Diäten für Hunde und Katzen.' *Nutrition*, No. 17 (1993), pp. 401–3.

Liberg, Olof: 'Courtship Behaviour and Sexual Selection in the Domestic Cat.' *Applied Animal Ethology*, No. 10 (1983), pp. 117–32.

MacDonald, David: 'The Pride of the Farmyard.' *BBC Wildlife*, No. 11, 1991, pp. 782–90.

Martin, Paul: 'The Four Whys and Wherefores of Play in Cats.' In: Peter K. Smith (ed.): *Play in Animals and Humans*. Oxford 1984.

May, Kimberley: 'Association Between Anosmia and Anorexia in Cats.' *Annals of the New York Academy of Sciences*, No. 510 (1987), pp. 480–2.

Merz, Ferdinand: 'Die biologische Funktion individueller Differenzen.' In: Amelang, Manfred and Ahrens, Hans Joachim (eds.): *Brennpunkte der Persönlichkeitspsychologie*, Vol. 1. Göttingen 1984.

Meyer, Wilfried: 'Zur Ernährungsbiologie der Wildfeliden. Part I: Einleitung und Kleinkatzen.' In: *Effem-Forschung für Heimtiernahrung*, Report No. 29 (1989), pp. 34–7.

Meyer, Wilfried: 'Zur Ernährungsbiologie der Wildfeliden. Part II: Grosskatzen, anatomische Besonderheiten und abschliessende Bewertung.' In: *Effem-Forschung für Heimtiernahrung*, Report No. 30 (1990), pp. 52–67.

Morris, James G.: 'Pet Food Protein: Current Use and Trends.' *International News on Fats, Oils and Related Materials*, No. 1 (1990), pp. 206–8.

Morrison, Adrian R.: 'Der REM-Schlaf bei Katzen.' *Spektrum der Wissenschaft*, June 1983, pp. 100–9.